Child Sexual Abuse within the Family

The Ciba Foundation is an international scientific and educational charity. It was established in 1947 by the Swiss chemical and pharmaceutical company CIBA Limited – now CIBA-GEIGY Limited.

The Ciba Foundation exists to promote international co-operation in biological, medical, and chemical research. It organizes about eight international multidisciplinary symposia each year on topics that seem ready for discussion by a small group of research workers. The papers and discussions are published in the Ciba Foundation symposia series. The Foundation also holds many shorter meetings (not published), organized by the Foundation itself or by outside scientific organizations. The staff always welcome suggestions for future meetings.

The Foundation's house at 41 Portland Place, London W1N 4BN, provides facilities for all the meetings. Its library, open seven days a week to any graduate in science or medicine, also provides information on scientific meetings throughout the world and answers general enquiries on biomedical and chemical subjects. Scientists from any part of the world may stay in the house during working visits to London.

Child Sexual Abuse within the Family

THE CIBA FOUNDATION

Edited by Ruth Porter

Tavistock Publications   London · New York

First published in 1984 by
Tavistock Publications Ltd
11 New Fetter Lane, London EC4P
4EE

Published in the USA by
Tavistock Publications
in association with Methuen, Inc.
733 Third Avenue, New York, NY
10017

© 1984 The Ciba Foundation

Printed in Great Britain
at the University Press, Cambridge

Library of Congress Cataloguing in
Publication Data

Child sexual abuse within the family.
Bibliography: p.
Includes index.
1. Child molesting – Addresses,
   essays, lectures.
2. Sexually abused children – Care
   and treatment – Addresses,
   essays, lectures.
3. Problem families – Services for –
   Addresses, essays, lectures.
I. Ciba Foundation.
HQ71.C57 1984   362.7'044
84-18918

ISBN 0-422-79280-2
ISBN 0-422-79290-X (pbk.)

British Library Cataloguing in
Publication Data

Child sexual abuse within the family.
1. Child molesting
I. Porter, Ruth II. Ciba Foundation
362.7'044   HQ71

ISBN 0-422-79280-2
ISBN 0-422-79290-X Pbk

Contents

Contributors

Members of a study group that met at the Ciba Foundation between September 1981 and March 1984

Dr Arnon Bentovim, Consultant Psychiatrist, The Hospital for Sick Children, Great Ormond Street, London WC1N 3JH

Detective Chief Superintendent John Bissett, Devon and Cornwall Constabulary, Middlemoor Police Station, Exeter EX2 7HQ

Professor Sydney Brandon, Department of Social Psychiatry, University of Leicester, Clinical Sciences Building, Leicester Royal Infirmary, PO Box 65, Leicester LE2 7LX

Mr R James Christopherson, Department of Social Administration and Social Work, University of Nottingham, Nottingham Park, Nottingham NG7 2RD

Dr Christine Cooper, Children's Department, The Royal Victoria Infirmary, Queen Victoria Road, Newcastle upon Tyne NE1 4LP; at present at: 3 Kenton Road, Newcastle upon Tyne NE3 4ND

Dr Hugh de la Haye Davies, Police Surgeon, Creaton House, Creaton, Northampton NN6 8ND

Dr Tilman Furniss, Department of Psychological Medicine, The Hospital for Sick Children, Great Ormond Street, London WC1N 3JH

Mr Paul Griffiths, NSPCC, Birmingham Group, Morton House, 223 Bristol Road, Birmingham B5 7UB

Professor Lionel A. Hersov, Children and Adolescents' Department, The Maudsley Hospital, Denmark Hill, London SE5 8AZ; at present at: Department of Psychiatry, University of Massachusetts Medical School, 55 Lake Avenue North, Worcester, Mass. 01605, USA

Dr Anthony D.M. Jackson, Consulting Paediatrician, The London Hospital, Whitechapel, London E1 1BB

Ms Helena A. Kennedy, Barrister-at-Law, 14 Took's Court, London EC4A 1JY

Dr Margaret A. Lynch, Department of Paediatrics, Guy's Hospital, St Thomas Street, London SE1 9RT

Ms Carolyn Okell Jones, Child Guidance Training Centre, 120 Belsize Lane, London NW3 5BA

Dr Ruth Porter, Deputy Director, Ciba Foundation, 41 Portland Place, London WIN 4BN

Mr Dennis Tunney, Assistant Chief Probation Officer, Inner London Probation and After-Care Service, 2 Kimpton Road, Camberwell Green, London SE5 7UW

Mr Richard White, Solicitor, 16 Paynesfield Avenue, East Sheen, London SW14 8DW

Foreword

This book is the product of a Ciba Foundation study group. The purpose of these groups is to examine scientific and medical subjects that are of public concern. The members of the group meet regularly over a period of one or more years to discuss the chosen topic. They collect information, explore the subject through discussion of papers prepared by the members, and finally summarize their findings in a report or book.

The subject of child sexual abuse was thought to be suitable for this approach and, at the suggestion of Arnon Bentovim, the first meeting of the study group was held in December 1981. A further seventeen meetings were held over the following two and a half years. The members of the study group are all actively involved in the care and management of sexually abused children and their families. The professions represented include psychiatry, paediatrics, general practice, the social services, the probation service, teaching and youth work, the law, and the police service. Although it will be clear that certain chapters are written mainly by different individuals, the contents of the book are the shared responsibility of all the study group members.

It is an especial pleasure to acknowledge the debt that we owe to the late Professor C. Henry Kempe, from the National Center for Child Abuse and Neglect, Denver, USA. Professor Henry and Dr Ruth Kempe gave a seminar on child sexual abuse at the Ciba Foundation early in 1981. The study group was the direct result of that seminar. We would like this handbook to be a tribute to the contribution that Henry Kempe and Ruth Kempe have made through their research to the study and understanding of child abuse and, more recently, of child sexual abuse.

Objectives and content

This handbook has been prepared to provide guidance about what actions may be taken by the different groups of professionals involved in the management of sexually abused children and their families – the victims, the perpetrators, and the close family and friends.

We present our summary of the characteristics of these families, the ways in which sexual abuse in the family presents to professionals, and particular behavioural manifestations in child or family that should alert professionals to the possible occurrence of sexual abuse. We refer in the main to father, step-father/daughter, and father, step-father/son abuse because our clinical experience to date mainly encompasses these groups.

We consider management by examining how professionals and their different modes of intervention become inextricably linked with the family system and we suggest the steps that professional groups have to take if, rather than maintain a static situation, they are to produce change in the family dynamics. Inevitably this leads us to consider links with child physical abuse procedures, the operation of the legal system, and to a consideration of how services could be more effectively organized and the various resources pooled to meet the new demands that increasing recognition of child sexual abuse is making.

We present ways in which procedures and professional practice need to be modified to ensure that a therapeutic stance is taken and maintained in the centre of thinking and planning, and how police, legal, child care, and protection approaches can be combined to this end with health care and social services. A general plan of management is outlined.

We next consider the detailed planning at each phase of the intervention: the phases of suspicion or disclosure; the phases of investigation and ascertainment; and the phases at which therapeutic management is planned initially and carried out in the long term. We describe the tasks that are necessary for the different professionals at each phase and the difficulties they are likely to meet.

We give examples of a variety of treatment methods now being used in different parts of the country and by different agencies. Suggestions for prevention are made, and are linked in particular with sex education in schools and at home, the definition of boundaries between appropriate and inappropriate touching, and self-help.

We point out the specific responsibilities and tasks of the professionals who may come in contact with sexual abuse. These include medical practitioners, community health workers, field social workers and day and residential care workers, probation officers, the police, and teachers and youth workers. We review the information available on the long-term harmful effects on children who have been sexually abused – the justification for our recommending these tasks. We also describe resources that are available to help the child, adult, and family, and to assist professionals who, equally, need consultation and support.

The objectives of this book are not only to point to ways in which rational management can link together both statutory and therapeutic requirements, but also to encourage professionals throughout the country to devise imaginative plans to bring this about. Our aim is to help children and families caught in a long-standing pattern of sexual abuse and incest. We hope that the interest in the problem now being shown by many professionals and volunteers will result in therapeutic action that will in turn encourage those caught in the dilemma to come forward for help. A multidisciplinary approach that combines control with therapy will go some way towards reducing the sexual abuse that persists in the community, largely because of fear of punishment.

Overview

Henry Kempe, writing in 1979, described a specific sequence of developing stages when looking at the way the community recognizes the existence of the abuse of children.

Stage one: denial that either physical or sexual abuse exists to a significant extent. Abuse that is seen is felt to be due to psychotic, drunken, or drugged parents, or foreign guests, and nothing to do with the community as a whole.

Stage two: the community pays attention to the more lurid forms of abuse – the battered child – and begins to find ways of coping more effectively with severe physical abuse and, through early recognition and intervention, with less severe abuse.

Stage three: physical abuse is better handled and attention is now beginning to be paid to the infant who fails to thrive and is neglected physically. More subtle forms of abuse, such as 'poisoning', are recognized.

Stage four: the community recognizes emotional abuse and neglect and patterns of severe rejection, scapegoating, and emotional deprivation.

Stage five: the community pays attention to the serious plight of the sexually abused child.

Stage six: the guaranteeing that each child is truly wanted, and provided with loving care, decent shelter and food, and first-class preventive and curative health care.

If we ask how far we have progressed in this country, for example by examining the cases that have attracted public attention and been the subject of government inquiries (DHSS 1982), we can see that concern has certainly reached stage three. We have a system of area review committees and extensive guidelines for the professionals dealing with physical abuse through a case conference and key worker system, with inter-disciplinary work a prescribed if not always an achieved goal.

The most recent guidelines on the registration of child abuse, issued by the Department of Health and Social Services (DHSS 1980), stretch towards stage four by also indicating that emotional abuse and neglect require registration, and are therefore brought into the child abuse procedures. There are many problems attached to widening registration at this stage, both in connection with the definition of emotional abuse and with the establishment of criteria to show that parenting has failed to a significant degree. A number of attempts are now being made to face these problems (Bentovim and Bingley-Miller, in preparation; Royal College of Psychiatrists 1982; Trowell 1983).

When we turn to sexual abuse, stage five, we find equivocation and lack of clarity in official policy. For instance, although the DHSS (1980) guidelines indicate that emotional abuse and neglect now require registration and a case conference, the summary of this memorandum states:

'When the Department sought comments on a draft circular in December 1978, a number of the responses suggested that the sexual abuse of children should be included in the definition of child abuse and should be dealt with under child abuse procedures. The Department, along with other Government departments, is examining this suggestion which raises complex issues.' (DHSS 1980: 1, para. 2)

But the same document goes on to say that sexual abuse 'should not be registered as a separate category, though some aspects will fall within the criteria' of other forms of abuse.

This certainly does not grasp the nettle of Kempe's stage five, sexual abuse of children in the community. Many area review committees have been in grave doubt and confusion about how sexual abuse should be managed and some have dealt with this by ignoring the problem altogether.

The extent of the problem is demonstrated in Finkelhor's (1979, 1980) research on community samples in the USA. His results indicate that 19 per cent of women and 9 per cent of men report an experience of sexual abuse that appears to have had long-term harmful effects on self-image and the ability to make sexual relationships.

Preliminary results, also from the USA (Russell 1983), indicate a high proportion of cases: 38 per cent of women reported an experience of sexual abuse before the age of eighteen, and 28 per cent before the age of fourteen. Although we do not yet have this sort of information for the UK, a recent survey of young people who responded to a questionnaire based on Finkelhor's questionnaire in a teenage magazine (Baker 1983) showed that 1,152 of the 3,200 respondents out of a readership of approximately 150,000 described sexually abusive episodes during their childhood. This represents 1 in 130 of the total readership of the magazine as a possible minimum incidence in the country as a whole. If the North American experience is to be taken as a guide, the true figure for the UK is likely to be far greater than this.

When we turn to the way in which sexual abuse comes to professional notice and is dealt with in the UK, a survey of professionals by Mrazek *et al.* (1981, 1983) showed the lack of multidisciplinary collaboration in this field. One thousand and seventy-two cases were reported to Mrazek and her colleagues as having been seen between 1977 and 1978 by a selected group of professionals, including police surgeons, paediatricians, child psychiatrists, and general practitioners (an incidence of 3 per 1,000 children reported during childhood, less than half the number expected on the basis of Baker's (1983) survey).

The cases were defined under three categories:

Type I: Battered children whose injuries were primarily in the genital area.

Type II: Children who had experienced attempted or actual

intercourse or other inappropriate genital contact
with an adult (e.g. fondling, mutual masturbation).

Type III: Children who had been inappropriately involved
with an adult in sexual activities not covered by I or II
(e.g. coerced into taking part in pornographic
photography).

Detailed reports, when available, showed that 4 per cent of the
children had experienced type I abuse, 69 per cent type II, and 16
per cent type III; for 11 per cent the type of abuse was
unspecified. Contrary to popular belief the children featuring in
the survey were not usually seductive adolescents: 60 per cent of
the total group of children were over the age of 11; but 27 per cent
were aged 6–10, and 13 per cent were under the age of 6. The
youngest child in the survey was a 9-month-old girl who was the
victim of a type II abuse. Eighty-five per cent were girls and 15
per cent were boys. There was an overlap with physical violence;
about 10 per cent of the children with types II and III abuse had
also been physically injured.

It was also noted that, contrary to expectations, the proportion
of children who reported sexual abuse by strangers was 26 per
cent; in most cases the perpetrators were members of the
immediate family or individuals who were known and trusted by
the child: 43 per cent were within the child's family and 31 per
cent were family acquaintances. One-half of the perpetrators
within the family were fathers, one-quarter stepfathers, and the
remainder were siblings, grandparents, and (a few) mothers.
These are similar to Finkelhor's (1979, 1980) findings.

Another striking observation in this survey was the high level
of prosecution in these cases (40 per cent), often unaccompanied
by any psychotherapeutic or social work help. The rate of
referral to child psychiatrists was less than 11 per cent and there
were many cases where social work referral had not been made
either, the sole form of child protection being the prosecution and
imprisonment of the offender.

The anomalous situation therefore exists that at the time of this
survey children who were physically injured by their parents
were being managed by an inter-disciplinary conference, which
included social service and health professionals, and the police.
The conference, acting on guidelines (DHSS 1980), was able to
exercise discretion over issues such as police investigation and
prosecution, with emphasis on the protection of the child and

appropriate therapeutic and social work with the family. Whereas sexual abuse, which is potentially damaging but not life threatening, was being dealt with by police investigation and prosecution, with little in the way of therapeutic, child care or protective work, and limited inter-professional co-operation.

Many reasons for this state of affairs emerge from legal and professional practices, but the attitudes observed, with an emphasis on legal control, are reminiscent of those seen 15–20 years ago during the initial stages of the recognition of the physical abuse of children.

How can we explain the fact that families maintain a rule of silence for many years and professionals avoid involvement in a field of considerable distress and potential damage? Families are obviously fearful that exposure will lead to family breakdown, with fathers imprisoned and children in care. Silence and self-sacrifice seem preferable. Professionals mirror the families' behaviour by managing not to see or hear what is going on. A key issue contributing to the professionals' wariness of involvement is the discomfort of not knowing what degree of sexual contact is abusive and what is a part of the families' appropriate affection-ate contact (Pincus and Dare 1978). Families who are frozen and out of contact with each other need physical contact and nurture, and we rightly encourage a show of warmth, which inevitably encompasses stroking and touching, as part of normal care. The extent and nature of touching between parents and children varies in different cultures, but if we seem to be suggesting that children should be kept at a distance in order to avoid contact because it could be misinterpreted as sexual, we could be as guilty of deprivation as of going too far the other way.

It is sometimes difficult for professionals to determine what constitutes the dividing line between acceptable discipline and physical abuse, and equally it may be difficult to distinguish between affectionate and sexually abusive behaviour (Anderson 1979). However, when the boundary between the demonstration of affection and sexual stimulation or exploitation is crossed what occurs can be clearly seen as abusive. It is understandable that professionals remain confused and helpless in the face of the difficult decisions they have to make for individual cases, and that they deny or suppress whatever suspicions or evidence exist–literally they avert their gaze (Ounsted 1975).

Furthermore, groups such as the pro-incest lobby in the USA and the Paedophile-PIE-group in the UK see nothing harmful in

adult sexual interest in children (Cook and How
may actively promote and initiate sexual activities wi.
For such groups what is at stake is the 'sexual liberau.
children whom they see as being denied their right to full sexu.
satisfaction. The views of such groups tend to arouse great
controversy, incense the public, and further confuse the
professional.

Professionals need support at many different levels. They must
learn to recognize sexual abuse when it occurs and to read the
warning signals. They have to work in what is not only a most
distressing field but also one that touches their own lives in a way
physical abuse and neglect do not. At a time when society
encourages sexual fulfilment, it becomes more difficult to
maintain appropriate boundaries. Sex is a fact of life and we have
sexual feelings that may excite and worry us at any stage of our
work. We need to be aware of the morbid interest, attraction, and
curiosity – the voyeurism – that sexual advances by adults
towards children may incite in us. Additionally, the sexuality of
children and our own sexuality as children and as adults, and
towards children and adults, tend to blur the distinction between
client and professional. We have to recognize that the high
incidence of unreported sexual abuse means that a significant
number of professionals will themselves have been victims and
may be struggling with painful memories of a traumatic experience whilst undertaking training and work in the field. No
wonder it has taken so long for the sexual abuse of children to be
recognized in the community.

Apart from one or two periods in history, with few exceptions
every culture has a taboo on incest between parents and children
or on sexuality between those who are not allowed to marry. But
the taboo today is as much against talking about and recognizing
activities that are in fact widespread as against the sexual abuse
itself. When Sigmund Freud first heard his patients describing
sexual events, he believed that the sexual abuse of children must
be common although never discussed. In the climate of the time
and under pressure to withdraw his allegations, he later ascribed
his patients' descriptions to wishes and fantasies. It seems now,
however, that the patients may have been describing actual
events. There is, of course, ample evidence for the existence of
sexual wishes towards those individuals to whom a child is
attached. But there are clear differences between the behaviour of
a child who has fantasies of sexual abuse and that of a child who

has actually been abused. For the real victim there is a pattern of somatic and behavioural features which we describe in this book.

The high level of secrecy and failure to report and the uncoordinated punitive response of professionals mean that we must devise a response that brings together the work of all professionals involved and includes police, legal, child care, and therapeutic approaches. This approach will create a climate in which professionals are encouraged to recognize the sexual abuse of children, and to respond to the minimal signs, in a way that will ensure the safety of the child and initiate therapeutic work with the family. A non-punitive climate is also necessary to enable parents who suspect or are involved in sexual abuse to come forward without the fear that family breakdown and incarceration of the abuser are inevitable. The years of self-sacrificial behaviour that characterize these children will no longer need to continue until they are old enough to run away, make suicidal attempts, or escape from an intolerable situation into a worse plight of anti-social activities, prostitution, or drug or alcohol abuse.

To start to meet these needs the British Association for the Study and Prevention of Child Abuse and Neglect set up a working party to consider the issues, and a basic educational pamphlet was produced (BASPCAN 1981) outlining the main features of child sexual abuse and making some suggestions for the development of professional awareness, and for assessment and management. The extent of professionals' interest is shown by the fact that some 11,000 pamphlets have now been printed and distributed. At the same time there has been a steady demand for workshops and teaching events throughout the country. Television and radio productions, and newspaper and journal articles have drawn attention to what has obviously been a difficult area for many individuals. The result of all this has been a considerable upsurge of interest both in recognizing sexual abuse of children and in clarifying how and when to get help in dealing with the problem.

Where there is a well-organized humanistic approach that brings together statutory and therapeutic measures and includes self-help groups, an increasing number of individuals, both children and parents, come forward for help. After phone-in and television programmes or newspaper articles about child sexual abuse, a remarkably large number of individuals respond, describing long-standing painful memories of abuse and a deep sense of guilt and shame, and the traumatic effect that these have had on different areas of their lives.

Sexual abuse occurs in secret, is kept a secret by the family and is being kept a secret by society's attitudes and taboos.

Reports from the literature on sexual abuse in childhood reveal an increasing number of short-term and long-term harmful effects (Okell Jones and Bentovim 1984), including effects on mental health, on the capacity to form satisfactory sexual and satisfying marital relationships, and on the ability to bring up the next generation. We should also state that not all individuals are harmed by a long-standing sexual relationship with an individual of a different generation, even when they do not fully comprehend and have not been able to give informed consent to the relationship (Kempe and Kempe 1978). But many of these individuals *are* harmed and the idea that children and young people who complain of being involved in a sexual relationship are either fantasizing, or in any case will not be hurt, is increasingly challenged by clinical and research evidence. Anna Freud recently noted:

> 'Where the chances of harming a child's normal development are concerned, it [i.e. incest or other forms of child sexual abuse by parental figures] ranks higher than abandonment, neglect, physical maltreatment or any other form of abuse. It would be a total mistake to underrate the implication or frequency of its actual occurrence.' (Freud 1981: 34)

Sexual abuse of children is an uncomfortable fact of life that cannot be ignored if the community is to reach towards Kempe's final stage of ensuring that children are wanted, and are provided with care, nurture, and health. If the community, professionals, and non-professionals, hold that a child should not be physically abused to such a degree that his or her life is in danger, and should not be so neglected or rejected that physical and emotional development are impaired, then society must also be concerned about the child who has to adapt to a sexual relationship that may affect her or his potential for later sexual interactions and the capacity to bring up the next generation satisfactorily. The care of these children is at least as necessary as any legal remedy for an act still classed as criminal. Our aim is to show how unnecessary punitive action can be avoided and therapeutic help provided for the whole family.

Part One: Background

1   Definitions

'Sexual abuse is defined as the involvement of dependent, developmentally immature children and adolescents in sexual activities they do not truly comprehend, to which they are unable to give informed consent, or that violate the social taboos of family roles.' (Kempe and Kempe 1978: 60)

It is difficult to produce an all-inclusive definition of child sexual abuse but the Kempes' definition has proved a valuable starting point for our deliberation. We have found it useful to categorize various forms of child sexual abuse as follows:

INCEST

The legal definition of incest applies to acts of sexual intercourse between a man and a woman within the prohibited relationships. These are: (a) a man with a woman who is his daughter, sister or half-sister, mother or granddaughter; and (b) a woman over sixteen years of age with a man who is her father, brother or half-brother, son or grandfather.

Illegitimate children are covered by the law of incest but adopted and step-children are not.

Lesser sexual acts (i.e. not involving intercourse) between, for example, fathers and daughters constitute other offences such as indecent assault or gross indecency with or towards a child.

SEXUAL INTERCOURSE WITH CHILDREN IN OTHER RELATIONSHIPS

These are the relationships not covered by current incest legislation, including relationships with adopted and step-children. In such cases the offences of unlawful sexual intercourse and indecent assault apply. For both these instances, where intercourse is an essential part of the offence, it is sufficient to establish penetration.

Father/son relationships come within the offences of buggery or indecent assault, not incest or unlawful sexual intercourse.

OTHER FORMS OF SEXUAL ACTIVITY WITH CHILDREN

These include fondling, mutual masturbation, digital penetration, oral-genital contact, and involvement of children in photography or filming for pornographic purposes.

2 Presentation and indicators: vulnerability and socio-economic risk factors

Sexual abuse, unlike physical abuse, often presents in a veiled way. Although some child victims have obvious genital injuries, or conditions requiring medical care (venereal disease or pregnancy), relatively few show such florid clinical features.

A proportion of the cases of sexual abuse come to light through direct reporting to an agency such as the police, or to a general practitioner, by an adult or occasionally by the children themselves; but recognition in many cases depends on professionals being responsive to certain physical and behavioural indicators. Although it is impossible to produce a complete list of these indicators we note below the signs and symptoms featured most commonly in our experience. Some of the indicators, for example venereal disease in young children or trauma to the perineal area, should convince practitioners that sexual abuse has occurred until proved otherwise; others, such as recurrent urinary tract infections, precocious sexual play, or persistent running away from home, although not conclusive, should alert professionals to the possibility of abuse. Suspicion increases when several features are present together. We have included as indicators some very common conditions that only rarely suggest sexual abuse, to show the diverse ways in which a child who has been sexually abused may reach attention. We also describe a number of vulnerability factors that, when present, further increase the risk of sexual abuse. Indicators may be physical or behavioural and vary according to the stage of development of the child.

PHYSICAL INDICATORS

Genital and anal areas

1 Bruises, scratches or other injuries, often very minor, not consistent with accidental injury (masturbation by a child does not cause bruising).
2 Itching, soreness, discharge, or unexplained bleeding.
3 Foreign bodies in the urethra, bladder, vagina, or anal canal.
4 Abnormal dilatation of the urethra, anus, or vaginal opening.
5 Pain on micturition.
6 Signs of sexually transmitted infections.
7 Semen in the vagina or anus or on the external genitalia.

General

1 Bruises, scratches, bite marks, or other injuries to breasts, buttocks, lower abdomen, or thighs.
2 Difficulty in walking or sitting.
3 Torn, stained, or bloody underclothes, or evidence of clothing having been removed and replaced (e.g. vest inside out).
4 Semen on skin or clothes.
5 Pregnancy in teenagers, especially where the identity of the father is vague or secret.
6 Recurrent urinary tract infections.
7 Psychosomatic features such as recurrent abdominal pain or headache.

BEHAVIOURAL INDICATORS

Sexual

1 A child who hints at sexual activity through words, play, or

drawings; or at the presence of severe family conflict, family secrets, or puzzling and/or uncomfortable things at home but who seems fearful of outside intervention.

2 A child with an excessive preoccupation with sexual matters and a precocious knowledge of adult sexual behaviour; one who repeatedly engages in inappropriate sexual play with peers; a child who is sexually provocative with adults.

3 An older girl who behaves in a sexually precocious way. Many girls become 'street wise', experienced beyond their age in a manner that isolates them from their peers and attracts censorious or seductive behaviour from adults. Their physical contacts with others have quasi-sexual elements of which they are unaware, with embraces involving breast or buttock caressing, or other body contact. They may wear sexually provocative clothing or adopt revealing postures – the caricature of a 'vamp'. In many cases they have already accepted sexual contacts if not intercourse with people outside the family.

4 Requests for information about contraception are rare but may be a cry for help.

General

1 Sudden change in mood.

2 Regressive behaviour, e.g. sudden onset of bed-wetting or its persistence into the later school years.

3 Change in eating patterns: loss of appetite, faddiness, or excessive preoccupation with food.

4 Lack of trust in familiar adults or marked fear of men.

5 Disobedience, attention seeking or restless, aimless behaviour and poor concentration.

6 Severe sleep disturbance with fears, vivid dreams or nightmares sometimes with overt or veiled sexual content.

7 Social isolation; the child plays alone and withdraws into a private world.

8 Girl takes over the 'mothering role' in the family whether or not the mother is present.

9 Inappropriate displays of affection between fathers and daughters or mothers and sons, who behave more like lovers than parent and child. The father may be over-concerned about his daughter and may insist on accompanying her to the doctor for, say, contraceptive advice.

Behaviour especially noticeable in school

1 Poor peer group relationships and inability to make friends.
2 Inability to concentrate, learning difficulties, or a sudden drop in school performance. (For some sexually abused children school may be a haven; they arrive early, are reluctant to leave, and generally perform well.)
3 Marked reluctance to participate in physical activity or to change clothes for physical education, games, swimming.
4 Regular avoidance and fear of school medical examinations.

Behaviour in older children

1 Anti-social behaviour or delinquency in young teenagers. The sexually precocious behaviour already described. Promiscuity and involvement in prostitution may be ways of drawing attention to sexual abuse. In addition, the following may occur:

   a Hysterical attacks.
   b Truancy or running away from home.
   c Suicide attempts and self-mutilation.
   d Dependence on alcohol or drugs.

VULNERABILITY FACTORS

It was first suggested by Burton (1968) that certain children are more vulnerable than others, and this has since been supported by a number of writers, for example Finkelhor (1980, 1981). The increasing divorce rate and consequent reconstitution of families affects not only parent–child relationships but also relationships between siblings and step-siblings who may be widely separate in age.

Children who have been denied affection, either as a result of earlier experience or through a failure to meet emotional needs within the current family, are at risk (Burton 1968).

A child is at risk when a mother is punitive over sexual matters; not close or affectionate with the child; often ill or absent – rejecting or rejected by her family; poorly educated; socially isolated and with few friends, as often due to her withdrawal as to their rejection; depressed, psychotic, or dependent on drugs; and, most importantly, sexually abused in her own childhood.

When a mother withdraws from her family, her children and husband may turn to one another for support, practical assistance, or comfort and the foundations of an incestuous relationship are laid. In other cases a man deprived of his conjugal rights may turn to the nearest available source of gratification – a dependent child. Children in families where neglect is so great that absence, changes in behaviour, or even early pregnancy, pass unremarked are at risk from inside or outside the family. If these children are not valued as individuals, family members may not only abuse them, but also fail to protect them from abuse by members of the extended family, friends, visitors, or even strangers.

In sexually abusive families the father may seem authoritarian or, in contrast, excessively meek; his needs for affection as well as his sexual needs may not be met; he may be an alcoholic or dependent on drugs. These men may misunderstand the adolescent's behaviour and be sexually aroused by it; or physical chastisement may lead the perpetrator to the excitement that blends into sexual activity.

For step-fathers and foster fathers the problem does not seem to be only the absence of the biological bond. Step-fathers are often introduced into the family at, or shortly before, evidence of emerging sexuality in older children. These fathers may not have experienced the maturing effects of bringing up their own children, which strengthen the incest taboo, and they may already have experienced problems in their personal relationships. All these factors make them particularly susceptible to emerging adolescent sexuality.

SOCIO-ECONOMIC RISK FACTORS

It is important to realize that social isolation can occur not only in rural areas but also in urban conurbations and slums. Low social class, poverty, and overcrowding have been described as prominent factors in the occurrence of child sexual abuse in some studies but these findings have mainly been derived from court or prison settings. Such families, too, are more likely to come to the notice of health and welfare agencies than families from the middle and upper social classes. Other studies (Finkelhor 1979; Giaretto 1981b) have shown that child sexual abuse occurs in families from any socio-economic background. It seems, however, that in families where the father is out of work and experiencing financial problems, or is ill or injured, he will be more often at home and is more likely to be depressed or drinking excessively than his counterparts in full employment. These factors may lead him to molest his children.

These indicators do no more that sensitize professionals to the type of background that puts a child at risk of sexual victimization. We suggest, however, that preventive measures should be directed at this group of vulnerable children and their families.

3 Patterns of family characteristics[1]

The stereotype relationship pattern within a family where child sexual abuse is occurring is that of an authoritarian father and a mother who appears weak and dependent on her husband; she is seen as the parent close to the child involved in the abuse but unable to protect her or him. But this is not necessarily the case.

Furniss (1985) has noted that the emotional relationship pattern may be exactly the opposite of this stereotype: the mother in fact is far more independent; the father, despite his apparent dominance, is heavily dependent on his wife for emotional support, especially at times of separation. He is also often perceived by her as making excessive sexual demands. Child sexual abuse occurs in a family where the man feels sexually frustrated by his partner but cannot break away because of his own emotional immaturity.

Furniss describes two different sorts of sexually abusive families: in one the abuse seems to serve the purpose of avoiding open conflict between the parents and in the other of regulating it. Two different patterns of maternal behaviour occur in the two different types of family.

CONFLICT-AVOIDING FAMILIES

The mother clearly sets the rules for emotional relationships and for the way sexual and emotional matters are talked about. These mothers are emotionally distant from the daughter(s) involved in the sexual abuse although they may compensate by compulsive caretaking for the family. The distance between mother and daughter may be so great that even when the child tells her mother what is happening the allegations are dismissed. The problems are not discussed within the family and if the child is taken to the family doctor the purpose of the visit seems to be to seek professional confirmation for the mother's denial.

CONFLICT-REGULATING FAMILIES

The mother is deficient in practical as well as emotional support for the children. She becomes their 'pseudo-equal' and one of the children may take on the role of mother. Sexual matters are more openly talked about and there may be overt conflict, and violence, between the parents. The child is 'sacrificed' to regulate this conflict and to avoid family breakdown.

Daughters in the incest families described did not feel emotionally understood or cared for by their mothers. The mothers were looked on as emotionally rigid or distant; there was an openly hostile relationship between mother and daughter and/or the daughter's appeal for her mother's love had been rejected. If they seemed close, the child had become the parent figure to the mother. The daughters complied with their fathers' sexual demands. The taboo against talking about the incest prevented the children from being able to find any help inside or outside the family. All the girls blamed their mothers for not having protected them and for not making it possible for them to talk to anybody about their frightening or exciting experiences.

The reversal of roles between parents and child was disorientating and disturbing for the child. There seemed to be no difference in the range of standards of practical care between these and other families but, in terms of emotional dependence, the father was on an equal level with his daughter.

The breakdown of the taboo against incest had led to the creation of a new taboo, which ruled that family members, even those who were involved in the sexual abuse, were not allowed to name or even recognize what was happening. Secretiveness and silence denied the possiblity of looking at the true nature of the family relationships. Nor could the abuse be discussed with people outside the family for fear of punishment or other disastrous consequences.

As a result of these studies, Furniss (1985) suggests that the constellation that brings about incest between father and daughter is the combination of emotional dependence and incongruent sexual relationships between different generations in the family. The child is put in a confusing and undefined position in relation to her parents and siblings, and the confusion between practical care as a parent, emotional dependence, and sexual relationships is maintained by secrecy.

In the conflict-avoiding families although the parents may never discuss what is happening they both covertly agree on the role of the daughter in the family. This non-spoken collusion increases the father's emotional dependence on the mother and keeps him firmly bound to the family. Disclosure of the abuse during therapy leads to a major crisis and to the danger of the family breaking up.

In the conflict-regulating families, there is more awareness of the reality of family relationships and there is not the same degree of secrecy as occurs in conflict-avoiding families. All the same, the changes in family relationships during therapeutic work may threaten the foundations on which the family is built.

SEXUAL ABUSE TREATMENT PROJECT[2]

In this study fifty-five families, referred mainly by social services deparments, were seen during an eighteen month period between September 1982 and April 1983. Since this time the organizers of the study have received an increasing number of referrals from prison officers, general practitioners, and community health professionals, as well as from social service personnel.

The study revealed the inadequacy of the professional response. Some of the children had been separated from their families, in care for some years, and without therapeutic help or attempts at rehabilitation. Families had been split with little collaboration amongst professionals. The first task of the treatment project, therefore, was to help clarify the professionals' confusion. The large number of families referred in the first eighteen months of the study indicated the extent of the professionals' demand for help.

There were forty-six girls and ten boys in these families; 40 per cent of the perpetrators were fathers, 30 per cent step-fathers, 25 per cent other family members; only a few neighbours and strangers were involved. These proportions agree with those found in other studies. The study revealed other startling figures. More than one-half of the children were between the ages of eleven and fifteen on referral, and the abuse, which in the majority of cases had progressed to actual or attempted intercourse, had continued for between two and four years in just under one-half of cases; in 70 per cent of cases the abuse had started in children of less than ten years of age. These findings support the clinical observations that once a relationship between an adult and a child has progressed from affectionate physical contact (which can have erotic overtones and intensity) to an actual sexual interaction, it becomes a permanent ingredient of the relationship and can be self-reinforcing.

The project used a combined group approach for girls, boys, and parents to help each other, and a family approach for the families to help themselves (Giarretto 1981b). Help was possible even though some family meetings were held in prison; care proceedings were usually necessary to reinforce the treatment so as to ensure that family members accepted the reality of their need for help.

NOTES

1 This chapter is based on a sexual abuse treatment project at the Hospital for Sick Children, London. The project is described further on pp. 114,123, and in detail in Furniss, Bingley-Miller, and Bentovim (1984) and Furniss (1985).
2 From the Department of Psychological Medicine, Hospital for Sick Children, Great Ormond Street, London.

4 Sexual abuse through generations

A range of confused and deviant sexual attitudes and behaviour may be generated in the children of sexually abused parents. At one extreme we see inhibition, over-sensitivity, and protectiveness and, at the other, chaotic and early involvement in intrafamilial sexual activity.

It is not uncommon for a father to molest sexually a succession of girls in the family, sometimes during the same time period but more commonly in sequence according to some arbitrary age limits. A child may be introduced to sexual activity at, say, seven or eight years of age and passed over in favour of a younger sister when she reaches that age. Group sex is rare, but multiple continuous assaults may occur, each victim engaging in a secret relationship apparently unknown to other members of the family. Sexual abuse may continue into adolescence or even into adult life.

Many abused girls engage in early sexual activities with males outside the family. These girls often become promiscuous and early pregnancy results with consequent escape from the family home. The girls maintain contact with their parents, despite their strongly ambivalent feelings for them, and their own children are often frequent visitors to the grandparents' home. The grandfather may then begin a further sequence of sexual molestation on his grandchildren, often initiating them at a younger age than their mothers. The response of the previously assaulted mother to the violation of her own children is often unexpected and directed towards protection of the perpetrator.

Men who abuse both their male and female children are more often violent and likely to extend their activities outside the family. In the more psychopathic families, with changing or multiple partners, male and female children may be involved in sexual activity with individuals of either sex. For example, a boy may be sexually abused by his father and involved in a variety of sexual activities with his father's mistress. It is not surprising that children subjected to such abuse not only become confused about their sexual orientation but also themselves become sexually abusive and feel that their adult status gives them the right to sexual dominion over younger children.

Girls who have been sexually abused may become sexually inhibited and in marriage abhor and try to avoid sexual activity. More commonly they embark on sexual activities early and with many partners. The first group may have children but are parsimonious in their sexual activity; the second may attract sexually aggressive and demanding partners. In either case the result may be a male partner who seeks sexual gratification from the children. These mothers may emulate the hated behaviour of their own mothers and deny the existence of the incest. It may be unnecessary to postulate unconscious mechanisms for some mothers will say: 'I knew what was happening but we can't manage without him', or 'I couldn't bear to go through all that again.'

For many of the victims the continuing sexual assaults of childhood are a guilty secret they have never been able to share. They regard themselves as spoilt, debased, and violated, and experience a bewildering complex of guilt, anger, and shame. Some never acquire a positive self-image. The models their parents presented are confusing: the abusive, hated, and sometimes violent father may have provided the only support and affection they received; and they feel out of touch with their apparently distant mother. Problems in mature relationships and neurotic symptoms are common.

The promiscuously sexually active girl may never reach orgasm, and a satisfying heterosexual relationship eludes her. She may marry and have children in the hope that this will 'cure' her only to find a distressing inability to express love for or receive love from her children, or to protect them.

It is not surprising that the mothers' chaotic feelings about sexuality should affect their children. These mothers may be revolted by physical contact and prudish in the extreme. They are distressed by nudity in toddlers and horrified by childish sexual curiosity or self-manipulation. Their children are over-protected but also vulnerable for they are brought up without even elementary knowledge about their anatomy and physiology yet vaguely aware of mysterious, frightening sex in the world about them.

5 Short-term and long-term effects[1]

There is dissension about the impact in later life of sexual abuse in childhood. One body of opinion sees nothing harmful in children having sexual experiences with adults (see p. xx) while another sees childhood as a treacherous and vulnerable time in the development of sexuality, and a time in which children need protection from premature sexualization and sexual traumas.

EFFECTS IN CHILDHOOD

We know that children are sexual beings but we must also recognize that sexuality in infancy and childhood, and in adult life, will be different. Child sexual abuse violates the dependent child's expectations of parental care, leading to confusion of roles and boundaries for the child, the family, and the next generation (Furniss 1983).

There is also the ethical issue of whether children can freely give consent to sexual activities with adults, particularly their parents. In a child–adult encounter, 'consent' may well represent an abuse of power. Nor can young children give 'informed' consent as they are not informed about sex and sexual relationships. Children may acquiesce, co-operate and sometimes even enjoy the sexual experience (Yates 1982), but they are not in a position to give free, informed consent. Even if they play an active part in the sexual acts they are not responsible for the adult's response. Sexual abuse that occurs in a context of warmth, bribery, the granting of special privileges, and (typically) extreme secrecy may be as traumatic and bewildering to the child as violent molestation (Fritz *et al.* 1981).

Many children accept the sexually abusive relationship for years, but with increasing recognition as they get older that something is wrong. Eventually they may suddenly disclose what has been happening to them, for example in a desperate attempt to protect a younger sibling from similar abuse or when a father's possessiveness and jealousy become unbearable.

It is hardly surprising that the child victims of sexual abuse show a great deal of anxiety. An adolescent girl appears proud of her power over her father and other men but underneath this facade she is in need of affection. These girls may sexualize all their relationships because they feel this is the only way to obtain love. Such children continue to have difficulties in giving and receiving love when placed in alternative families and may try to enact, with foster parents, previous sexual experiences (Yates 1982). They also have difficulty in expressing anger because of the intensity of their angry feelings towards their mother for failing to protect them, as well as towards their father. They are often depressed and confused. They tend to adopt attitudes of self-sacrifice, either passively withdrawing or acting out in a self-destructive, flamboyant manner. Suicidal attempts are not uncommon (Goodwin 1981) and young adolescent victims in families that have disintegrated and where the mother has clearly blamed the child are most at risk.

Sexual abuse can no longer be dismissed as a temporary problem. The extent of its long-term effects depends, probably to a large extent, on its early recognition and treatment.

EFFECTS IN ADULTS

Most clinical studies describe three patterns of adult sexual behaviour in the victims of child sexual abuse.

1 Promiscuity, often associated with alcohol and drug abuse.
2 Sexual coldness and failure to form lasting sexual and emotional relationships.
3 No ill-effects.

Studies of the effects of sexual abuse in childhood in psychiatric patients (Lukianowicz 1972), in patients in psychotherapy (Meiselman 1978, Herman 1981), in psychoanalysis (MacCarthy B.F., personal communication; Steele and Alexander 1981) and in individuals presenting as physically abusing parents (Goodwin 1981) all show sexual and emotional problems. These studies, however, are all of abnormal individuals. It is more difficult to find control populations – individuals who were sexually abused in childhood but have not been adversely affected – for comparison. A few studies using non-deviant adult populations have now been published. Finkelhor (1979) administered a questionnaire to college students; and Tsai *et al.* (1979) compared individuals who felt damaged by their experiences, a 'clinical' group, with a matched group who did not. Tsai and her colleagues noted a more frequent and longer duration of molestation, with intercourse more likely, in the clinical group. The girls who had no symptoms in adult life had had support from friends and family during childhood and had not been blamed for the events; they also had found sexual partners in adulthood who were sympathetic and understanding.

Adults who have been sexually abused in childhood have a poor sense of their own worth; they are often depressed; they describe a sense of pollution, contamination, and dirtiness. Frequently the victims feel abandoned by their mothers and recreate essentially abusive relationships in their search for a cure.

Sexually abused parents often abuse, physically and sexually, their own children. They experience physical affection towards their infants not as nurturing but as having a sexual meaning. Sroufe and Ward (1980) observed that these mothers may 'unconsciously' use seductive methods of disciplining their children. They combine severe physical punishment with, for example, direct kisses on the child's mouth and stroking of their genitals – a repetition of their own experiences.

The evidence so far suggests that sexual abuse may have lasting adverse consequences in adult life, especially on sexuality and the ability to bring up children. Further studies, particularly of less severely affected and seemingly unaffected individuals, are now needed.

NOTE

1 This chapter is based on a longer paper with additional references (Okell Jones and Bentovim 1984).

Part Two: Management – general
principles

6   Introduction

The discovery of a case of child sexual abuse inevitably causes stress for all concerned and it is important that those involved are clear not only on the procedures to follow but also on their professional implications. The roles of the different professionals involved are set out in detail on pp. 92, 106. General aspects of these tasks and the dangers at different stages from the first suspicion that child sexual abuse may be occurring to the long-term management of child, victim, and family, are illustrated schematically in the chart (see p. 26).

We wish to emphasize the need for co-operation between the different professionals and agencies at all stages. While the unique contribution of each profession is recognized, the needs of the victim and her or his family must supercede inter-agency rivalry.

time (days)	0 ——→ 1	——→ 3	——→ 21 plus
stage	suspicion, disclosure	initial case management preliminary investigations and interventions	long-term management
key activities	listen	co-operation, planning future management (including case conference)	plans put into action (including case conference)
key dangers	panic, precipitate action	insensitive (precipitate) action	giving up (because of poor expectations of success)
	THINK	THINK (ACT)	ACT (THINK)

Figure 1 Tasks for professionals at the three stages of management of child sexual abuse

7   Links between professional
and family networks[1]

When professionals intervene in an incestuous family, the family
ceases to be autonomous. A professional–family system is
created. The influence of the professional network on the family
processes is a crucial element in the work with families in which
sexual abuse of a child has occurred.

FORMATION OF THE PROFESSIONAL–FAMILY SYSTEM

Once the sexually abusive relationship is revealed publicly, a
number of professional agencies intervene. This results in
changes in the family system and in the network of professional
agencies. The abuse becomes a multi-professional as well as a
family problem, and the reactions in the professional system
directly influence family relationships and the social and emotional interactions between different individuals within the
family.

Professional intervention never involves one source or person.

Usually, a number of individuals from different disciplines and agencies, and from voluntary organizations and self-help groups, become involved. Different professionals tend to become identified with different individuals within the family. The professional agencies develop a system of operation that is separate but not independent from the family operations. Each system immediately begins to influence the other, with resulting changes in the professional network as well as in the family.

Processes in one system tend to be mirrored in the other. For example, at the moment of disclosure the father is often seen by other family members as entirely bad and solely to blame for the family crisis, whilst the mother is seen as entirely innocent and good and the daughter is seen as the victim who may also be contaminated by moral evil for having yielded to her father's advances. The professional system may reflect this pattern by putting the father into prison, leaving the mother at home, and taking the child out of the family into care, for protection from her father but also for her own good. The father may be humiliated in prison, particularly by his fellow prisoners; and the girls are closely and often suspiciously watched by professionals, for example the staff in a children's home.

There are three basic types of professional intervention and each of these leads to specific changes in the family. The type of intervention influences whether the family relationships revert to the original balance of conflict avoidance or regulation (see p. 12), whether the family falls apart, or whether therapeutic change can be achieved so that the family can live together without the abuse.

Each type of intervention deals differently with questions of responsibility, activity, guilt, and blame and is distinguished according to particular aims towards different family members. The three basic types of intervention are:

1 *Primary police intervention* Any intervention by any professional with the father as its target and his punishment as its aim. This type of intervention assumes that the perpetrator carries sole responsibility for what has happened. It sees the roles of different individuals in the family as fixed properties rather than pointing to the changing interactions between family members. Primary police intervention is not a property of one particular professional agency (i.e. the police) but

indicates the way the abuse is viewed.

2 *Primary social services intervention*   Any intervention where the child is the target of direct action with the declared aim of protecting her or his physical, emotional, and moral development.

3 *Primary therapeutic intervention*   Any intervention that aims to change family relationships and includes all family members.

In practice, all these elements usually coexist.

PRIMARY POLICE INTERVENTION

Any police intervention has by definition to be punitive when unlawful acts are involved. The sexual abuse of the child is dealt with by removing the father from the family. This enables the mother and daughter to scapegoat the father and to mask their own guilt feelings and their sexual competition for him. The daughter's accusations against her mother for having exposed her to the abuse are easily covered through apparent closeness between mother and daughter and their agreement that the father is not only responsible for the abuse but also the only guilty person.

PRIMARY SOCIAL SERVICES INTERVENTION

The social services, like the police, have statutory obligations. They use their power to act as 'better parents' for the child in competition with the parents. This type of intervention is directed against the parents in order to protect the child. The underlying implications are that both parents have failed. However, this concept allows that two family members are involved and moves towards a family understanding of the abuse.

Although in theory the aims here are to protect the child from the parents, in reality the threat is to the child, removing her or him from the family with consequent separation from the mother, siblings, friends, and the wider social environment. For the family members who remain, the removal of the girl is easily interpreted as expulsion of a core of moral evil from the family. Once the child has left, the parents can cover up and deny their own emotional and sexual problems and scapegoat the child. She is victimized in two ways. She feels punished and blamed by being separated from her family; and, at the same time, she is prevented from resolving her confusion about the abuse because this cannot be dealt with outside the family.

PRIMARY THERAPEUTIC INTERVENTION

The purpose of this form of intervention is to change the family relationships and the underlying psychopathology that led to and maintained the abuse. It is not directed towards any particular individual but towards the entire family. It does not aim at legal and punitive actions although it may need legal measures to back up treatment and will use temporary separation of family members if this is helpful.

At first it might seem that the father and daughter are most in need of treatment; from the outset, the father's responsibility and the daughter's involvement are obvious. However, as the therapeutic intervention proceeds, the mother, initially regarded as the person least involved, often becomes central. Three major problems in the relationships between mother, father, and daughter may appear during therapy: the mother's failure towards the daughter in preventing the abuse; the competition between mother and daughter as female partners for the father; and the emotional and sexual conflict between the parents. After the initial focus on the father and daughter, the mother may find herself in the most stressful situation. The family can influence the professionals to a greater extent in this type of intervention model than in the other two.

THE INFLUENCE OF THE PROFESSIONAL NETWORK ON THE THERAPEUTIC SYSTEM

Type of intervention

The primary therapeutic intervention does not exclude other types of intervention agencies, that is the social services or the police. On the contrary, if the therapeutic intervention is to have any chance of success the plan of approach and the extent of involvement of the professional agencies must be agreed at the very beginning. Legal back-up is often needed so that treatment can proceed.

Consistency during the intervention

A family member can involve other professionals outside the therapeutic setting if the boundaries kept by the professionals are not carefully observed. The sudden departure of, for instance, a key social worker can destroy the consistency of the initial intervention and the trust between the family and the professionals. It is, therefore, important that the same individuals should remain throughout the acute crisis and the early stages of treatment. It may be impossible to bring family members back into therapy after they have once left it.

Interference with the therapeutic system by other professionals

There are two types of interfering systems: (a) a professional involved in the treatment colludes with a family member against the therapeutic team; and (b) previously uninvolved professionals intervene and try to take over. For example, disruption can be caused by professionals and family members colluding to change the previously agreed treatment plan. Uncoordinated and unexpected interventions by outside agencies, for example sudden police or child care actions, are examples of the second type of interference.

THE INFLUENCE OF THE FAMILY ON THE THERAPEUTIC SYSTEMS

Attempts to 'run away' from therapy

We anticipate that at some point in treatment each family member will try to opt out. One of the most striking influences on the professionals is when family members and even the father try to turn the therapeutic intervention into a primary police intervention. At this stage the therapy has become so emotionally unbearable for the father that to face the shame and responsibility for his actions is a greater punishment than imprisonment, and he chooses prison.

Attempts to change the nature of the intervention

The family reacts actively to the way in which the professional network intervenes. A primary therapeutic intervention may be changed into a primary police intervention, as described, but family members may also try to change the therapeutic intervention into a social services intervention, and remove the child from family therapy.

THE INTERLOCKING PROCESS IN THE THERAPEUTIC SYSTEM

Furniss (1983) describes an example of the complex interlocking process between family and professional systems. A change in the crisis therapeutic team (two staff members absent) led to a take-over by other professionals. This resulted in control being assumed by one of the daughters. She changed the form of intervention from the therapeutic to the police type. The father was imprisoned and treatment was effectively stopped. The father's removal led to changes for other individuals in the family. The mother was desperate on her own and moved closer to her daughter. This complex process involving both family and professionals was initiated by one family member with the aim of changing the alliances within the family.

In systems theory terms, the developing conflict between professionals was in fact a family conflict by proxy. The police acted on the daughter's behalf and the crisis team acted for the father. Father and daughter were struggling to make the mother their ally and she was being pushed and pulled between the two of them.

If the professionals cannot agree about the meaning of the conflict, that is if they cannot see that they are enacting a family conflict by proxy, they will try to take different actions directed against separate individuals. The decisions of the professionals then become bureaucratic, based on the rules of their different agencies, and therapy cannot proceed. The process of identifying a conflict by proxy is one of the key issues during treatment. Professionals must not be drawn into such a conflict but must provide the framework for therapeutic renegotiation of family relationships so that the family can find its own therapeutic solution.

NOTE

1 This chapter is based on a study at the Hospital for Sick Children, Great Ormond Street, London. For further details see Furniss (1983).

8   Legal problems in
         child sexual abuse[1]

The vulnerability of children has made it necessary to formulate special offences to protect them from physical and sexual abuse. The first response of the law has been to punish the offender and the second has been to provide ways of removing the child from the harmful environment. A third response, which has been developed from the study of physical abuse or non-accidental injury, has been to improve the environment in order to prevent further abuse and to preserve what is good within the family setting. This approach is still new to the courts in their consideration of sexual offences, and what must be examined is where such an approach would be appropriate and what legal framework would be required for such cases. Choosing what to do in any individual case presents serious difficulties in principle and in practice. The major concern must be for the child. It is clearly necessary to retain the notion that sexual abuse of a child is a crime as much for the need to define the limits of acceptable behaviour towards children as for the deterrent value. It is equally necessary to ensure that criminal law and civil family law combine to provide a framework which promotes the welfare of the child.

CRIMINAL PROCEEDINGS

Once the 'crime label' is accepted, the well-established investigation, trial, and sentencing procedures for crime come into operation. Society demands that its disapproval of certain behaviour is reflected in the criminal process. The defendant who is subjected to the criminal process is entitled to the protections and safeguards developed over centuries to prevent miscarriage of justice. The victim is entitled to justice as well as to the opportunity of reducing to a minimum the ill-effects of the crime. It is difficult in an area that still evokes such overwhelming outrage to justify the mildest reform even where it might be in the interests of the victim. A system of checks and balances is essential in the interests of all.

There are four areas to be examined in the criminal process:

1 Investigation
2 Decision to prosecute
3 Trial
4 Sentencing

Investigation

In the UK there is no obligation to report crime. It is not an offence if a relative or social worker does not go to the police when incest or another sexual offence is suspected, though agencies such as the National Society for the Prevention of Cruelty to Children (NSPCC) may have their own internal requirement to report. Failure to act by a professional person is also likely to invite judicial criticism if it comes to light in adverse circumstances. The wall of silence surrounding sexual abuse within the family seems solid and reinforced by the fear of the consequences that follow discovery. This fear would be greatly diminished if it were understood that the courts, where possible, inclined towards treatment rather than imprisonment, towards rehabilitation rather than punishment.

The investigation must take account of legal, criminal, and

civil aspects and allow for a medical examination. Inevitably the police will have primary involvement in an investigation.

The role of the police

Under the Prosecution of Offences Regulations 1978 the most serious offences have to be reported by the police to the Director of Public Prosecutions (DPP), but in all other cases the police have a discretion as to whether or not they should prosecute. Decisions will vary not only between different police forces but also between different persons in a force to whom this duty has been delegated.

In recent years about 300 cases of sexual abuse within the family have been brought to the notice of the police throughout the UK annually (Cmnd 9048 1979–82) but it is clear that there is no consistent approach to their investigation and prosecution. These discrepancies should be remedied by creating much clearer guide-lines for all police forces and by adopting the proposals of the Royal Commission on Criminal Procedure (Cmnd 8092 1981) to separate the investigative from the prosecuting function by creating Prosecution Departments for all police forces in England and Wales.

The police would be left with complete responsibility for investigating offences and for making the initial decision to start criminal proceedings, to caution people instead of prosecuting them or to take no action. Once the decision to prosecute had been taken by the police, the Crown Prosecutor would take over responsibility for the case. He or she could then withdraw the charges altogether, modify them or, of course, proceed as decided by the police. The Crown Prosecutor would also take any pre-trial decisions that might arise and be responsible for the conduct of the prosecution at the trial.

In essence the Royal Commission is proposing a system in which the Crown Prosecutor would have similar responsibilities locally to those which the DPP has nationally. The police would retain unimpaired their law enforcement role and the primary reponsibility for bringing offenders to court.

However, under these proposals, if an offence is arrestable, then *any* officer from the chief constable to the most junior constable, for example a police officer on the beat (whether in uniform or in the criminal investigation department (CID)) could make the decision to arrest. In cases of child sexual abuse it must become established practice that decisions to arrest and charge are made in conjunction with an officer of senior rank. This is the most important stage in the procedure and a wrong decision can have disastrous consequences. In some forces there is already the practice of liaising not only with senior officers but also with agencies such as social services or the NSPCC before decisions are made. This is the most enlightened approach and there should be a requirement to liaise in this way save in cases of emergency.

If through the decision to arrest and charge, an innocent man is prosecuted, his personal life and the lives of those near to him could be seriously harmed, even if he is eventually acquitted or the charge is dropped. On the other hand, uncertainty and indecision may lead to the non-arrest and non-charging of a man or woman who may then proceed to commit further offences.

An example of what can be done is seen in the county of Devon. The police force and social services department have developed an impressive procedure for dealing with cases of child abuse, both physical and sexual. The police force recognizes that child abuse is an emotive subject and that each case raises complex issues that can only be resolved by close co-operation, liaison, and team work amongst the organizations concerned. With this in mind certain officers in the force are now designated *child abuse liaison officers* in each of the health districts within the county. In the county of Devon, due to the fact that so much stress is placed by the various agencies on co-operation and co-ordination, it was decided to call their meetings *co-ordinating meetings* instead of case conferences as laid down in a DHSS Home Office circular (1976).

Members of the Devon constabulary are as aware as anyone else that the immediate and long-term interests of the child are of paramount importance, but it should also be understood that the police have a reponsibility to investigate suspected offences and prosecute where necessary. However, even when prosecution does become necessary, the intention is to liaise with the other agencies at every stage before a final decision is made.

Any disagreement at co-ordinating meetings is recorded and, if not resolved and a member wishes, will be passed to an area appeal panel. This will be convened under the chairman of the area review committee within seven days, and consists of the professional heads of the agencies involved, the chairman of the co-ordinating meeting, the person wishing to appeal, and any other members of the co-ordinating meeting who have a material contribution to make. If a unanimous decision is not reached the matter must be referred to the county appeal panel immediately and will be dealt with within seven days. This body is chaired by the chairman of the county review committee and consists of the professional heads of appropriate agencies. In addition, the chairman of the previous meetings attends, together with any other person whose contribution is likely to be material. The decision of this group is final but if agreement still cannot be reached the police file will be forwarded to the DPP. Points of disagreement will be set out in the accompanying correspondence. To date this has not been necessary.

Set out below are the procedural instructions issued to police officers in Devon in cases of child abuse (*Devon Multi-disciplinary Child Abuse Handbook*, 1984: 83–4). We recommend that these should be adopted nationally. These instructions refer to physical, emotional, and sexual child abuse and neglect.

'Immediate action

1 On receipt of information that a child has been the subject of an act of deliberate abuse on the part of the parents, guardians or any other persons, the police have a duty to investigate the allegations.

2 The investigation of all child abuse cases will be carried out by experienced police officers and/or senior detective officers, with the detective officer of the division concerned maintaining direct supervision.

3 The child abuse liaison officer or the senior divisional criminal investigation development officer must be informed immediately when any case of suspected child abuse is reported or information is received.

4 The liaison officer must inform the social services co-ordinator (child abuse) immediately so that a coordinating meeting can be arranged.

5 The liaison officer must keep the coordinator informed as to the progress of all investigations.

6 The police will not act unilaterally except in respect of an emergency case which is initially reported to them.

7 Officers must consider whether a police place of safety order

will provide sufficient time to complete the investigation, or whether a magistrate should be asked to issue a (longer) place of safety order (Children and Young Persons Act 1969). [A place of safety order ensures that a child or young person is detained in a 'safe' place without the consent of the parents, for up to eight days by decision of the police, or for up to twenty-eight days by order of a magistrate.]

8 In circumstances where a child is not in immediate danger, the child abuse liaison officer must be informed immediately so that the social services coordinator (child abuse) can be asked to arrange a coordinating meeting.

Subsequent action

1 Although the child abuse liaison officer should attend coordinating meetings and reviews, some coordinating meetings are held in respect of children who are at risk but who have not been abused and, therefore, unless the police have some family background knowledge which may assist, there is no need for a police officer to attend.

2 The liaison officer and/or investigating officer attending coordinating meetings and reviews should be prepared to give verbally any relevant information they have on the family.

3 The social services coordinator (child abuse) must be notified of change of circumstances after a child's name has been placed on the child abuse register.

4 The police will maintain records of confirmed and suspected cases of child abuse and respect the confidential nature of other information received at meetings.'

Guide-lines for the conduct of the investigation

1 The police officers involved should receive special training.

2 A suitable adult should be present when a juvenile suspect or victim is interviewed.

3 Interviews should, in general, not take place at the police station.

4 The medical aspects have to take account of two needs: the immediate physical examination; and the child's welfare in the long term.

5 The alleged perpetrator will be questioned at an early stage. He should be advised to have his solicitor present. Contemporaneous notes of interviews must be written, preferably with tape-recording, and the alleged perpetrator should be invited to sign the record of interview.
6 Where possible bail should be considered so that time is adequate for deciding whether or not prosecution is appropriate. Clearly this will depend upon the availability of a suitable residence – possibly the home of a relative or a hostel – and the prevention of harmful contact between those involved. The interests of the child are paramount.

The immediate physical examination (for details see pp. 94–5) Consent for a general medical examination must be obtained from the victim herself (especially if she is fourteen or over) and from a parent or person acting *in loco parentis* when the child is young. If the child refuses to be examined, that may be the end of the matter. If a parent refuses to permit the examination, the medical practitioner will consider whether other legal consent can be obtained through the courts; very occasionally the doctor, after consultation with colleagues and, probably, his defence society, may be obliged to take personal responsibility for a decision to examine the child without parental consent.

Decision to prosecute

A humane and discriminating prosecution policy must be justified in the interests of the victims themselves and this at least is endorsed by the Criminal Law Revision Committee (1980) which expressed the view that the intervention of the criminal law should be as limited as possible in practice and that sentencing should be particularly flexible.

A large number of minor offences can be dealt with by cautioning but the extent of the use of this practice varies considerably between police forces. In Devon and Cornwall the caution is used in a high percentage of first offences in general crime and in appropriate cases of child abuse. It is to be hoped that this procedure will be extended. The introduction of independent prosecuting authorities would provide a channel of consultation that could be used before charging.

Sometimes, of course, haste is essential, for example if there is a danger that the suspect will commit further offences, interfere with vital witnesses, or otherwise impede the investigation. The decision to charge is crucial. Every effort should be made to ensure that the decision is made only after careful deliberation by experienced persons. The sensitive nature of child sexual abuse cases calls for special care.

Where channels of liaison are established and the case appears to be one where the protection of the child is more important than successful prosecution but a charge has already been laid, the independent prosecutor could decide to offer no evidence or, if in a crown court, have the case left on the file. Where this latter procedure is adopted with the agreement of the court, the matter cannot proceed later without the leave of the Court of Appeal. Clearly a prosecutor is only likely to take this course in accordance with the principles laid down by the DPP, whose criteria place great emphasis on public interest.

The factors that can properly lead to a decision not to prosecute will vary from case to case but broadly speaking the graver the offence, the less likelihood there will be that the public interest will allow of a disposal less than prosecution (e.g. a caution). However, the views of all the agencies concerned should have enormous influence, which is why it is so important to establish channels of communication between all those involved professionally.

Trial

The adversarial system of English law relies upon each side in a case having the right to test the evidence of their opponent by way of cross-examination. Fundamental to the criminal process in serious cases is the right to trial by jury and the right to be acquitted unless the prosecution proves its case.

Evidence

Where the allegation is of a sexual offence there has to be corroboration of a material nature. This can be medical evidence, albeit of a general kind, or may be of things seen or heard that could point to the truth of the allegation. It is a legal principle that no one can be convicted on the uncorroborated evidence of a child. A child's story always needs corroboration. In cases of suspected incest, however, the nature of this corroboration may consist in the child simply telling an adult, if this is done soon after the alleged event and the story is reasonably objective – a description of emissions, say. Evidence from another child or finding child-pornographic literature may also count as corroboration. In general, evidence from a three-year-old child cannot stand without additional objective evidence, for example semen present; verbal evidence from a child of about nine years may stand with corroboration, as described; a sixteen-year-old (or older) child's evidence stands without additional corroboration. Before the trial ever takes place, committal proceedings in the magistrates' court determine whether there is sufficient evidence to justify a prosecution (a prima facie case). This is often a formality but the defence can require a complainant to attend to test the evidence even at this stage (Magistrates' Court Act 1980).

Any reform of trial procedure involves a balancing act between the interests of a witness and the rights of a defendant. For any victim of a sexual offence the trial procedure is painful but many of the suggestions to reform it totally undermine the rights of defendants to a fair trial by a jury: for example hearings before judges alone in a formal setting (family court); jury behind a viewing panel; hearings before a panel of magistrates.

A further proposal is that the complainant need not be cross-examined. Affidavit evidence could be presented on behalf of the child, or evidence given by a child psychiatrist, who has interviewed the child, with a video recording of the interview. But it is fundamental to the rights of the defendant that he (or she) is given the opportunity, if he (or she) so wishes, to test the evidence of the child.

Improvement in present judicial systems

We believe that a number of changes can be made to improve the judicial system, both in and out of court, and to civil proceedings as much as criminal proceedings.

In many cases an early, sensitive therapeutic approach is in the best interests of all concerned. However, it must be recognized that legal difficulties can arise. There is no problem in the case where a decision is taken not to prosecute at all, but where the criminal process is invoked there must be concern to prevent contamination of evidence. If a father, albeit under the supervision of a psychiatrist, is able to present to a child his account of events, the temptation is great for the child to adjust her or his own account to recover the affection of the parent. Alternatively, the family hostilities uncovered in the therapy sessions may encourage the enlargement of the allegations. The possibility of contamination of the victim's evidence would have to be relevant to the considerations of a judge and jury in a criminal trial. Its effect could be to render unsafe the evidence of the victim and perhaps that of other family members whose evidence might have provided corroboration.

Unless there are bail conditions preventing contact, those having the care of the child and those advising the father could arrange a therapeutic meeting, notifying the police about this. This should only be done in the knowledge that it may affect any intended prosecution.

Expedited hearing procedure

This is a better way of ensuring early therapeutic involvement and our major proposal is to create a specially expedited process for cases of child sexual abuse. The Scottish courts enforce very strictly the rule that cases must be brought to trial within 110 days of arrest. This is for *all* criminal cases. A similar strictly applied rule should exist nationwide in cases of child sexual abuse, with the period of three months delay after charge being the maximum permissible. The effects of such a strict rule are multiple. In fully contested cases, where the defendant's challenge to the evidence may reflect an unwillingness to face his (or her) own behaviour and suggest, therefore, a low likelihood of success in therapeutic work, the child and other family members are at least saved some of the horrors of delayed trial. Memories are still comparatively fresh and psychiatric and social work help for the child and the rest of the family can be firmly established.

If the defendant is frankly admitting the allegation, intends pleading guilty and wishes to participate in the therapeutic process, a special procedure to expedite the case to an even earlier date should be available on the application of the defendant after consultation with his (or her) legal advisers.

Psychiatric and social work help should commence with the child soon after discovery. For this reason it is essential that where possible the child's evidence and that of witnesses in the family, for example siblings, should be taken *in full* by police before treatment begins. In this way professionals such as psychiatrists can feel uninhibited in their work; and the allegation at any subsequent trial that the child's evidence developed in response to suggestions made during treatment is avoided.

We suggest that where the defendant elects to enter an early unequivocal plea of guilty in a case of child sexual abuse there should be an automatic six-week period of assessment either on bail or in custody. The purpose of this assessment would be to determine the appropriateness of a therapeutic programme. A probation officer would be the co-ordinator between psychiatrists, social workers, and whichever agencies were involved with all the parties. A social enquiry report would condense all the information received and would present to the court the recommendations of those involved, and outline the programme if a non-custodial sentence could be contemplated. Sentence always rests with the judge and even in the face of professional recommendations he or she may take the view that imprisonment is the only suitable course. Lawyers and the judiciary will be educated in their approach to cases by their contact with psychiatrists, other doctors, social workers, and probation officers. It is, therefore, imperative that arguments in reports are well supported and written in clear language and that recommendations are not wholly unrealistic.

There is a very small group of solicitors who will seek and a small group of doctors who will provide medical reports and recommendations that owe more to the adversarial nature of the judicial system than to the reality of the situation. Such reports may limit themselves to particular aspects of the defendant's history or mental state and give little weight to the best interests of the child, or recommend treatment programmes that cannot be achieved.

Wherever possible the expert witnesses in a case should have had an opportunity to participate in a case conference or co-ordinating meeting with other professionals before appearing in court. In this way genuine differences of view could be presented to the court but they would be on the basis of knowledge of the total facts and available resources.

Creating a special expedited hearing procedure in cases of child sexual abuse would not necessarily require legislation; a directive from the Lord Chancellor to the courts' administrators could achieve the same result.

One of the concerns about creating expedited procedures is that a defendant may feel pressurized to plead guilty to avail himself (or herself) of a non-custodial option. For this reason the defendant must have access to early legal advice. To establish that the plea of guilty is unequivocal at any application for expedited hearing the defendant would be specifically reminded of his (or her) rights to contest the case. The defendant's legal representatives would present to the court a declaration that advice had been given and unequivocally received by the defendant.

No proposals are perfect but preventing delay is one method for reducing a major area of anguish that can often undermine therapeutic work. It also creates a way to establish therapeutic work with the whole family as early as possible without trampling on the rights of defendants to a fair hearing.

The contested hearing

Before the hearing children should be able to wait in a private area where they will not have to come into contact with the alleged perpetrator or with defendants from other courts. There should be provision for the child to be with the 'most suitable adult'.

It is important to prepare a victim for the trial by providing clear information about what to expect. Unfortunately, the rules do not allow a prosecuting counsel to do more than introduce himself or herself to lay witnesses for the Crown, to avoid any suggestion that there has been 'coaching'. We recommend that the prosecuting solicitor or solicitor for the local authority discuss in advance with the child what will happen in judicial proceedings.

A better atmosphere for the child could be created by hearings without wigs and gowns, using simple language and conducted in less oppressive courts where parents and social workers can be present and near to the child witness. The reticence to recount graphic details is made the greater by the formality of the court and the proximity of the accused. We also recommend that the judge has discretion to conduct the court in such a way that account is taken of the welfare of the child. The judge already has power to clear the public gallery and direct the press not to publish names when a child is giving evidence and we argue for this to be done as a matter of course in cases where the complainant is a child or young person (see Children and Young Persons Act 1933). A special situation arises where the abuse is within the family because the complainant's anonymity is lost as soon as the alleged offender's name is published. Particularly in cases where treatment in the form of family therapy follows, publicity of any sort can be very damaging. We therefore urge general anonymity in cases of child sexual abuse.

There will inevitably be cases where the child has to give evidence, and she or he can then expect to be cross-examined. During cross-examination it is usually suggested either that the child has been indulging in flights of imagination, is fantasizing, or is unstable or mad; that she or he is sexually promiscuous; or vindictive and deliberately lying. Not surprisingly such questions and insinuations are quite devastating to the truthful witness whereas the defence counsel whose client says he (or she) is innocent will not be affected.

Lawyers should be educated to use a more sensitive approach when cross-examining children and judges encouraged to intervene to protect child witnesses from insensitive handling by lawyers from either side. Increasing use could be made of child advocates or other forms of representation to ensure the protection of the child. Even more important, educating the judiciary towards a new approach to sentencing will persuade many offenders to plead guilty at the outset (see below).

Sentencing

The principles of sentencing are:

1 Punishment
2 Deterrence
3 Rehabilitation

The answer judges give when presented with a highly charged plea of mitigation recommending rehabilitation rather than punishment is that they have a duty to the public to deter others from committing the offence in question. The sentencing policy of the Court of Appeal on sexual offences is generally to imprison – both to punish and to prevent repetition of offences. Changing sentencing policy involves a steady programme of education for the judiciary and the public at large. The recent attempts by the government to encourage a reduction in prison sentences have met with little success because of resistance by judges to any interference with their discretionary function. In general, a sentence of imprisonment follows upon conviction of sexual abuse of a child. The courts have yet to be persuaded that such a sentence may serve to break up the family in a damaging and distressing manner. Most prison sentences have a destructive effect on the families of the offender. Ideally judges should become convinced that the long-term effects for the child victim of sexual abuse within the family are in a special category and can be more damaging than the sexual acts themselves. A punitive attitude towards child sexual abuse does not serve aggressor, victim, or community.

We realize, however, that problems of sentencing in this class of case are very difficult. Cases involving violence or seduction of very young children, or multiple offending, will require imprisonment, but most sexual abuse offenders within the family are not dangerous criminals. Rationally the appropriate sentencing should reflect these facts, but the impulse of the general public is that the child sexual abuser is a monster who should be locked up. Although sentencing policy may be ahead of public opinion, as for example in the case of the abolition of the death penalty, policies usually reflect the repugnance felt by most people for certain offences. It is for this reason that sentencing changes will have to be married to a programme of public education. Judges will require carefully prepared professional opinions to support any decisions not to imprison and, once again, we wish to highlight the importance of the role of the team of professionals. Each individual case must be carefully distinguished in view of current public concern.

A sensible approach to sentencing is the most effective way of reducing the numbers of contested cases. This is also the best way of decreasing trauma for the child both by reducing her or his guilt about the parent and also by removing altogether the deleterious court experience. There is no need for a victim to attend a hearing where there is no contest as the judge has before him or her the victim's written statement and the prosecutor informs the court of all relevant material.

The number of contested cases is currently small in any event because the Crown accepts pleas of guilty to lesser offences in an effort to avoid the need for children to give evidence. Offenders are also advised by their lawyers that sentence is likely to be affected by the decision to fight a case. Judges make it clear that they give discount where a defendant pleads guilty at the outset thereby protecting a child from the unsavoury experience of giving evidence.

The reason for contesting a case where the offender is guilty is usually to avoid imprisonment or because the offender cannot confront and admit his (or her) own behaviour. The former position would be met in many cases by a change in general sentencing policy. The latter problem is exacerbated where an arrested (wo)man is detained in custody and is isolated from all those persons concerned with the overall problem. As with the decision to prosecute, a well-functioning professional team may be able to influence sentencing.

More and more solicitors invite the assistance of a psychiatrist before trial but this is by no means always the case. For this reason, defence legal aid granted in the magistrates' court (for these offences) should automatically entitle the solicitor to obtain psychiatric assistance in preparing the defence. This is particularly important as the very contact with a psychiatrist can help a defendant decide to plead guilty.

Probation and suspended sentence orders

Much of the research in the USA (see e.g. Giarretto 1981b) indicates that conviction is an essential prerequisite for treatment. The main reason for this is that even when offenders go into therapy voluntarily, they often back out of the sessions when these become emotionally threatening.

We are satisfied that the present arrangements for a probation order with a requirement of treatment provide a satisfactory means of engaging the offender in treatment for a period of up to three years. The individual must consent to treatment before such an order can be made and in our view it should be possible to include in the contract between offender and therapist the requirement that the probation officer will be informed if the offender does not co-operate in the treatment process. In that event the probation officer may arrange for the offender to be brought before the court either for a modification of the order, for example a new condition of residence, or for sentence on the original offence.

The professions and the public at large need to be made aware that a probation order with a requirement for treatment is not a soft option. Breach of the order can be dealt with using the full vigour of the law on the basis of the original conviction.

A suspended sentence cannot be of more than two years. A suspended sentence supervision order is possible if a sentence of more than six months is suspended but there is no mechanism for requiring treatment and the suspended sentence is activated only by commission of another offence.

A sentence may be deferred for up to six months to enable the court to take account of the offender's conduct during deferment or of any change in his (or her) circumstances. This might be used to test an offender's commitment to treatment or to enable suitable measures to be taken to protect family members. However, the judiciary are unlikely to defer sentence to permit a trial of treatment and there seems no advantage in a deferred sentence over a probation order with a requirement of treatment.

There are two problems that may arise with a probation order with a requirement of treatment. First, in the event of non-co-operation or other breakdown of treatment, the therapist has no direct access to the court. It is the responsibility of the probation officer to decide whether or not the individual is in breach of the order and should be brought back before the court. A difference of views between professionals can arise; or a change in probation officer during the time of the order, for example, might result in differences in the decision about whether to take further action. The second and more fundamental problem is raised by an irrevocable breakdown in treatment not occasioned by failure of the perpetrator to attend. Such breakdown might result from many factors, including intransigence on the part of the perpetrator, but this does not represent a breach of probation and cannot be dealt with by the courts. Thus treatment failure may leave the subject at liberty and unchanged in attitude, to the detriment of victim and family.

There appears to be no satisfactory solution in law to this dilemma. We suggest that doctors should only undertake such treatment programmes as a requirement of a probation order if they are confident that the victim can be adequately protected regardless of treatment outcome. In addition, the family must give fully informed consent in writing to release the doctor from normal requirements of confidentiality: that the doctor may report to the probation officer, the police, or the social service department any information that suggests that any family member is at risk of harm. This might lead to prosecution for further offences or, for instance, to the taking into care of a child victim now being scapegoated within the family.

Civil proceedings aimed at safeguarding and promoting the welfare of the child victim may proceed at the same time as criminal proceedings. They require proof of circumstances only on the balance of probabilities and not, as in criminal matters, beyond reasonable doubt. Thus while both types of proceedings might be necessary and desirable, and there may need to be liaison between the prosecutors of both sets, they are not dependent on one another.

Care proceedings

The most likely legal action by the local authority is to take proceedings in the juvenile court, where the authority may obtain a care order authorizing it to act as if it were the child's parent.

The difficulty in these measures is that they may depend on evidence available only to the police, who are not prepared to provide it before the case comes up in the criminal courts. The welfare of the child may require that civil proceedings are not delayed until after the criminal proceedings. It may be possible to continue without police evidence, if it can be demonstrated by other means that the grounds for care proceedings are substantiated, though some juvenile courts seem reluctant to accept this.

If police evidence is essential to care proceedings, there seems to be no reason why the police should not be required to give evidence on witness summons if the court can be persuaded to hear the case. There will be a greater reluctance to hear the case if the defendant's rights are prejudiced (note the recent letter of guidance on this subject from the Scottish Home and Health Department's Social Work Services Group (SWSG 1982). This is one example of how we place more weight on protecting the rights of a defendant than on securing the welfare of the child.

Wardship

In complex cases involving the sexual abuse of children, wardship may better promote the welfare of the child. Theoretically, wardship procedures are subject to the same problems in considering evidence that will be used in the criminal proceedings. However, the court will give directions for the care of the child when the parent or parents are unable to care.

There may be advantages in wardship over the more usual care proceedings for cases of sexual abuse. If necessary, injunctions may be made that control the movements of the parties in relation to the child. Conditions comparable to bail could be imposed but in a form, if necessary, to last longer than would be possible under the criminal law. The extent of the powers of the High Court has not yet been established, but there seems to be no reason why it should not accept a parent's undertaking to receive treatment as a condition of working towards the rehabilitation of perpetrator and victim in the family. If this is not achieved, the court could make alternative orders for placement of the child.

Planning the future

If the local authority decides to use the more usual juvenile court proceedings and exercise its powers under a care order (or interim order) it should consider what steps it wishes to take in the child's interests. It should decide at an early stage whether rehabilitation is in the child's interests, notwithstanding the outcome of criminal proceedings. If the aim is for rehabilitation, it may be necessary to make this known to the prosecuting authorities and the court, and to seek non-prosecution or a sentence most appropriate to the interests of the child and bail terms that reflect the ultimate plans. If the child is to live with the other parent but apart from the perpetrator, it may be necessary to ensure that the parent who retains care obtains satisfactory civil court orders. It may also be necessary to ensure that this parent understands that the authority will not accept that the child lives with the offender again and that it has powers to seek removal of the child if the offending parent returns. If the authorities decide that it is not in the child's interest to live with the parent again, they must immediately make plans for the child's long-term future.

CONCLUSIONS

Many of the problems considered are relevant to both criminal and civil proceedings. Promotion of the welfare of the child is as important as prosecution of the perpetrator. We have emphasized the importance of the welfare of the family in prosecution policy and the need for liaison between the authorities responsible for prosecution and those responsible for the welfare of the child and the family.

NOTE

1 Since this chapter was written, the Criminal Law Revision Committee's fifteenth report – on the subject of sexual offences – has been published (Cmnd 9213 1984). Information on further proposed changes in the law are included in the report.

9 Professional attitudes and co-operation

These comments have been prepared following consultations with the Joint Co-ordinating Committee for the Defence Unions and a number of other appropriate individuals and organizations. The reader is also referred to the section on sentencing (pp. 45–9).

The General Medical Council's (GMC) (1983) current guidelines on professional conduct state:

'confidential information may also be shared with other persons (nurses and other health care professionals) who are assisting and collaborating with the doctor in his professional relationship with the patient. It is the doctor's responsibility to ensure that such individuals appreciate that the information is being imparted in strict professional confidence.'

(GMC 1983: 19 (2) (b))

Further guidance is given in this matter in the same document:

'Rarely, disclosure may be justified on the ground that it is in the public interest which, in certain circumstances such as, for example, investigation by the police of a grave or very serious crime, might override the doctor's duty to maintain his patient's confidence.' (GMC 1983: 20 (2) (g))

'Whatever the circumstances, a doctor must always be prepared to justify his action if he has disclosed confidential information.' (GMC 1983: 20 (3))

Case conferences

It is essential that all participants in a case conference and in the case management that follows accept the need for the highest level of confidentiality. This is best achieved where good local inter-professional relationships have been developed. Senior members of each profession should be designated to meet regularly and advise on practice, the same designated individuals to be available for reasonable lengths of time.

Written minutes should be sent only to the people at the case conference and should not be duplicated although they need to be available for each individual's parent agency. Members of the conference should be reminded, at the start of every meeting, of the crucial importance of confidentiality.

It may also be necessary to designate case conference minutes and some or all of the confidential information provided by individual practitioners as highly confidential and to be specifically excluded from any agency policy permitting access to the records by local councillors, other departments, or by the clients themselves.

These comments on confidentiality in connection with child sexual abuse are already accepted practice in other forms of child abuse and neglect. Guidelines were set out in a DHSS circular to local authority social services nearly ten years ago, as follows:

'*Confidentiality*

25. . . . the safety of the child must in all circumstances be of paramount importance and must override all other consider-

ations. It is nonetheless undeniable that there will be occasions when the need to protect a child will conflict with the wish to preserve a relationship of trust with another party, and that the problems posed by confidentiality admit of no easy solution, although it is important to work towards solving them. Any decision about the release of information is normally one for professional judgement but the factors which ought to be taken into account in reaching such a decision are the "need to know" and the consequent restriction of information to those directly concerned with the family and who have the duty legitimately to perform a service on its behalf; and the importance of taking action in a child's best interests in the light of all relevant facts. It would be helpful if the passing of information between the caring professions were regarded and treated as analogous to that passed in confidence within a single discipline. Whenever possible, however, an adult's agreement should be sought to the sharing of information about him with professionals from a different discipline.

Case conferences

26. The case conference is recognised in all areas as a vital process in handling cases of children injured, neglected or at risk.' (DHSS 1976: 2(iv))

Disclosure of sexual abuse by an adult patient

An individual may seek help from a doctor because of guilt or anxiety associated with the sexual abuse of a child. He or she may reveal their activities under the influence of drink or drugs, for instance after a self-poisoning attempt, or during the course of psychiatric treatment. In these circumstances the interests of the patient and the child concerned, who is not the patient, will conflict.

In our view the protection of the child must take precedence over other considerations. The doctor should first try to obtain the patient's consent to report the abuse, probably to a case conference. If there is no immediate danger of the abuse continuing the therapist might wish to discuss the matter with colleagues, with his or her defence society, and with the patient's general practitioner. If the patient's consent is withheld, the doctor may decide that the greater good will be served by reporting the sexual abuse. Medical defence societies would support such action if they were satisfied that the practitioner had acted in good faith. They would prefer to know of such action in advance but this is not obligatory.

Non-medical professionals can probably act within these guidelines but consultation with a senior colleague and a professional organization is usually advisable.

10 Organization of therapeutic and investigative services

Child sexual abuse is an emotive issue generating distress and uncertainty amongst professionals who may feel ill equipped to deal with these cases because of lack of expertise, inadequate resources, or anxieties about bureaucratic reactions. There should be an experienced, trained, multidisciplinary group available in all areas to provide advice and support for the professionals who have to deal with such cases.

The identification of this group and its role in service and education must depend on local factors. In some areas more than one such group may already exist while in others there may be none and a small group must start *ab initio*, the members educating themselves and co-ordinating professional effort in their area. The area review committees initially established to deal with physical abuse should concern themselves with sexual abuse and encourage the development of local services. All professionals in the area should be aware of the existence of these groups and know how to contact them.

CO-OPERATION BETWEEN PROFESSIONALS

In each area social workers, doctors, community nurses, and police should meet to discuss their respective tasks. The primary task must always be to protect children from further abuse, and admission to a hospital or other place of safety should be available without difficulty or delay when required.

There will be considerable differences in philosophy and practice between and within the various professional groups and these should be recognized and articulated. It is more important to establish good relationships between the professionals than to strive for arbitrary consensus or spend major energy in perfecting bureaucratic procedures.

Through education and supervision all professionals should understand that when child sexual abuse is suspected or detected action must be taken *at once* to seek advice and establish whether a child is at continuing risk. Although it is important to avoid precipitate action, if immediate steps cannot be taken to protect the child within the home or extended family, admission to a safe place should be arranged.

No one should be allowed to deal with a possible case merely by writing a letter to the director of social services or referring the problem to another specialist. This could mean delaying whatever action is needed. Child sexual abuse should always be treated as an urgent matter requiring immediate consultation with a specialist or group with appropriate expertise.

To some extent procedures will depend on the resources available to support the child care system. The availability of therapists with special experience in, for example, family therapy may mean that a family can be treated with the prospect of rehabilitation within the legal framework whereas in another area rehabilitation may not be practicable.

Once child sexual abuse has been confirmed and protection of the child assured, some workers should concentrate their efforts on the perpetrator and other family members. Other professionals must focus on the child victim, helping her or him to understand and come to terms with what has happened. Anxiety, guilt, and ignorance, and the premature arousal or distortion of sexual feelings all require explicit discussion with the child. Above all these children need help to achieve the confidence to assume responsibility for their own bodies and to learn how to rebuff inappropriate advances.

SUPPORT AND SUPERVISION

One therapist, whether social worker, general practitioner, or hospital specialist, should not assume sole responsibility for the management of a case of child sexual abuse. A multidisciplinary approach is needed, although the key worker or co-ordinator concept is useful. Any therapist, especially one who deals with the family over a long period of time, will need professional support and supervision, not least in dealing with their own feelings. The emotional demands made by these families are considerable. Another problem of the intense and long-term involvement in working with these families is the tendency to over-identify with one individual in the family and to be drawn into the collusive behaviour patterns within it. Denial of continuing abuse, sexualization of relationships, and emotional disengagement despite continuing 'therapy' may be more easily identified by a supervisor or colleague than by the therapist working directly with the family.

A different hazard occurs when a worker without the necessary training or skills, and with no outside support, tries to provide counselling or therapy for young victims or their families. Where there is no appropriate language and no clear objective, 'therapy' sessions may continue over quite long periods without the sexual abuse that led to the request for help being made explicit.

RELATIONSHIP TO EXISTING CHILD ABUSE PROCEDURES

There are similarities and differences in the management of sexually abused and physically abused children.

The safety of the child

In cases of physical abuse, ensuring the immediate safety of the child usually means admission to hospital, if necessary under a place of safety order. In child sexual abuse, investigations are needed to establish whether or not there is a prima facie case before deciding that action to protect the child is required. Such investigations should always be regarded as urgent and if there is any delay, interim arrangements to protect the child may be necessary.

The medical examination

It is usual to arrange a medical examination as soon as possible in cases of suspected physical abuse but in many cases of child sexual abuse there is not the same urgency. (The medical examination is described in detail on pp. 94–5).

The police and social services

Children who have been physically abused usually come first to the attention of the social or medical services. The police are not involved until the case conference, unless the injuries are very severe. A child who may have been sexually abused, however, is usually referred first to the police, rather than to other agencies, through a parent or the child making a direct complaint. In sexual abuse cases, therefore, the police inform the social and medical services, rather than the other way round, and police investigations start earlier. When a child who has been sexually abused is referred to other professionals, early contact with the police is necessary to co-ordinate investigations and establish a prima facie case. Joint interviews between police and social workers are helpful. Where sexual abuse has occurred within the previous forty-eight hours, immediate police action is essential, in particular to obtain the necessary forensic evidence. The establishment of appropriate evidence is also important for the maintenance of the therapeutic programme for the child and the family.

With physical abuse, provided the child is in no further danger and other agencies are taking an active part, the police can exercise discretion and defer any necessary action until after the case conference. In cases of sexual abuse, too, especially where the allegations concern events that took place months or even years before, the police could defer action until after the case conference. Unfortunately, although some enlightened police forces use such discretion, many take action immediately, often with disastrous results.

Report to the Director of Public Prosecutions

Professionals, knowing that certain cases must by law be reported to the Director of Public Prosecutions (DPP), are reluctant to involve the police. Although at a local level they feel able to discuss matters with their local police officers, the remoteness of the DPP and the obligations of the police to follow his advice in relation to prosecution leads to the fear that the voices of local professional workers carry no weight, however sympathetic the views of the police in the area. Chief constables may in appropriate cases use their discretion and refer these cases to the DPP only when they genuinely need advice. Most forces have their own prosecution departments, where legal advice is good and the solicitors employed relate easily to local situations. This problem will only be resolved as police officers at all levels gain experience about the complex issues involved.

The ideal

A procedure that is already working well in some regions and could usefully be copied by all is the appointment of a senior officer as child abuse liaison officer, to be responsible for all cases of child sexual abuse (for details see p. 36).

The case conference

Although preliminary investigations by medical staff and social workers are undertaken before the case conference in cases of physical abuse, it is usually only at the case conference that full information is available and confirmation of the suspicion of physical abuse is made. In child sexual abuse much more detailed preliminary investigations are made by police, social workers, medical staff, and others. Preliminary, informal, multidisciplinary meetings are often needed to co-ordinate investigations and early intervention before the formal case conference is convened.

The objections of the unconvinced professional to involving the police are the same now with sexual abuse of children as they were with physical abuse during the 1960s. (Four cases are described in the appendix in which different actions by professional agencies, including the police, had very different results.) For physical abuse it has taken nearly twenty years for the role the police currently play to be accepted. If similar procedures are followed with sexual abuse – case conferences and inter-professional co-operation through juvenile bureaux and child abuse liaison officers – then it will not take as long to develop similar levels of mutual trust in respect of the sexual abuse of children.

Part Three: Management – in detail

11 Management at disclosure

Most cases of sexual abuse are diagnosed either as the result of specific allegations or from clues picked up during interviews with the client, patient, or pupil. The initial purpose of the interview may seem unrelated to sexual abuse. In some cases suspicion is aroused by the child's behaviour or by knowledge of predisposing factors within the family. Finally, evidence of physical injury may be found in the course of a general examination.

PHYSICAL MANIFESTATIONS

Where a child has received severe injuries as the result of a sexual assault she or he is likely to be taken by a parent or other caretaker to a hospital accident and emergency department. Even when injuries are restricted to the genital area, the diagnosis of sexual abuse can be missed if explanations about falling astride a sharp object such as a fence are accepted unquestioningly. Where the more obvious injuries are not in the genital area, evidence of sexual abuse may be missed altogether if it is not looked for routinely. Careful inspection of the genital and anal areas in every paediatric examination will identify a very few children with abnormalities caused by sexual abuse. Less severe injury, bleeding, or soreness may be discovered in the day nursery or school and advice sought from social and medical services. Such 'minor' injuries and psychosomatic complaints may also be shown without explanation to a doctor or health visitor.

A child who has been sexually abused may present with venereal disease. This should be considered in all cases of vaginal discharge in children and appropriate investigations carried out.

There must be a readiness to include sexual abuse in the differential diagnosis of children presenting with psychosomatic problems (see p. 6). Gaze aversion (Ounsted 1975) is especially likely in these cases. For example, a medical student, as part of a paediatric project on recurrent abdominal pain, had made a number of home visits. She reported a ten-year-old girl who had attended an outpatient clinic several times with a history of recurrent abdominal pain and intermittent vaginal discharge. The child, she was told, would not go to sleep at night unless someone, usually the father, lay in bed with her. The mother, herself frequently ill, expressed concern about signs of puberty in her daughter. When the student described her findings to her supervisor he, at least at first, seemed not to want to hear about them and literally 'averted his gaze'.

VERBAL DISCLOSURES

While the discovery of injuries or venereal disease may precipitate verbal disclosure of sexual abuse, the verbal account usually comes first and with some children it is the only evidence that abuse has occurred.

Disclosure to a professional can come from the child, the perpetrator, another member of the family, or a family friend or neighbour. Any professional involved in the care of children and families can be a target for a disclosure and should be prepared to receive and act upon the information. For example, when a mother decides to act upon her knowledge of sexual activity between her husband and child, she may go to the local police station or take the child to the family doctor or to a hospital casualty department. If the child is young, she may confide in the health visitor or day nursery matron; with an older child, she may ask a teacher what to do. If the family have a social worker or the child is seeing a paediatrician or child psychiatrist, the mother may hint at the problem during a visit. Often a sensitive or trusted adult in the child's world simply gets a hunch that something is wrong through the child's drawings or play.

Unfortunately many professionals feel uncomfortable discussing sexual abuse. The adult or child who is trying to tell them what is happening will quickly sense this reluctance and change the subject of conversation using some excuse for having requested the interview. All too often the possibility of sexual abuse never enters a professional's mind.

When the symptoms or behaviour of a child suggest sexual molestation this should be mentioned to the parents. In families where there is no sexual abuse the parents usually take this calmly, assuming that you are implying a perpetrator outside the nuclear family. But in families where sexual abuse is occurring the perpetrator may violently deny this, assuming that an accusation is being made against him (or her). This may result in a closing of ranks within the family, including denial or retraction by the child. Abuse is likely to continue after this and steps must be taken to protect the child.

Disclosure by the child may be the first indication that she or he is the victim of sexual abuse. An older child will be able to give a verbal account of what has occurred. A younger child may impart the information through play or drawing. When the abuse has been diagnosed because of injury or the revelations of an adult, time must be spent in getting the child's account of the events for legal and therapeutic purposes. If sexual abuse is suspected because of a child's symptoms or behaviour, opportunities must be given for the child to disclose what has been happening. For many professionals a major problem is finding the time needed to build up the child's confidence sufficiently for her or him to trust an adult and talk openly about what has occurred. Those talking with the child must be familiar with the child's personal vocabulary (see p. 112).

When a child gives an account of sexual molestation, she or he must feel believed. It is rare for such an account to be anything but the truth. One occasional exception is when a child is being used as a pawn in a custody dispute, but this is usually obvious because the language the child uses will be that of the coaching adult rather than her or his own.

We discuss below two examples showing the children's attempts to tell someone what has happened to them.

Case 1

Maria, aged twelve, made references over a period of ten months to 'goings on at home' to Mrs B, a grandmotherly figure, whose role was to escort Maria between home and special boarding school. At the end of every holiday Maria used to wait until the other children went to the station buffet and she was alone with Mrs B, then would say that she wanted to tell Mrs B something which must be kept a secret. Gradually Maria described games that her daddy used to play with her which he now played with her younger sister. The games involved lying close to daddy on the settee while he put his hands inside their knickers. Maria confided that she didn't want to play these games any more and that she wanted to keep 'that thing' for when she got married.

This information seriously alarmed Mrs B and her supervisor and it was conveyed to Maria's social worker, Miss E, who visited Maria at boarding school and took her out to tea. Miss E explained that Mrs B had told her that Maria was worried about some things that had happened in the past. Miss E then asked Maria could she think what these might be? Maria was silent but then said in a subdued voice: 'It's what daddy does with me.' With encouragement from Miss E, Maria proceeded to elaborate on this. She recalled that it began when she was about nine years old, before she went to her new school. Daddy started to pester her to do things with him and offered her money. He would wait until everyone was out of the house then he would ask her to go into his bedroom or he would go into hers. Sometimes she had her clothes on and sometimes just her nightie.

Maria said her father used to lie on top of her or tried to get her to lie on top of him; then 'he keeps trying to get it in me and although it won't go in he keeps on doing it'. She said this lasted for quite a while and came to a finish when 'the runny bit comes and makes my clothes wet'. When asked by Miss E how she felt about what happened, Maria said she didn't like it, it made her angry and sad and she wanted something to be done to stop it happening to her and her younger sister.

Case 2

In Sally's case it was an observant, sensitive teacher who discovered her predicament.

The problem came to light when Sally's male class teacher was off sick and a female supply teacher noticed Sally (aged nine) constantly whispering secrets to a friend. At the end of the school day she commented to Sally that she seemed to have lots of secrets. Sally agreed but said they were not nice secrets. The teacher suggested that if Sally could share these secrets with her friend then perhaps she could share them with her now. Sally then revealed that her father had had sexual contact with her. She said: 'Daddy's been very naughty, he hurt me with his finger. I didn't like it, he's done it lots of times before down there. Mummy went away – every time she goes away he does it. He took my pants off.' Sally added that she'd told her mum who'd said she mustn't talk about it and that she didn't understand now but that she would one day.

As often happens, at a later stage of investigation of the case, Sally became frozen in her responses, minimized what had happened, finally claiming that it had only happened once.

12 Talking with children

Talking and playing with young children or interviewing them about specific allegations of sexual abuse is a skilled, delicate, and to many practitioners a daunting task. Some practical suggestions for interviewing children are described below.

BEFORE THE INTERVIEW

Thought must given, before the interview, to what use should be made of information obtained, the actions that can be taken, and their consequences if a child does reveal that sexual abuse is currently occurring. The presence of another person, for example a trusted adult, particularly with a young child is helpful. If another professional can also attend, unnecessary repetition of the child's story may be avoided. The interview should take place in surroundings familiar to the child if at all possible.

THE INTERVIEW

It is easier to establish rapport with a child if the interview starts with general family topics: brothers and sisters, relationships within the family, how many rooms, who sleeps where. Questions about who cares for the child, who puts her to bed, and so on may follow before introducing more difficult subjects.

Sexual matters

An older child can often be helped to start talking about sexual matters by giving an example: 'You told your teacher/granny/foster-mother that daddy put his hand in your pants/showed you his penis and that this was bothering you. She thought it might help if we talked about what happened to you.' A younger child can first be questioned indirectly if an accompanying adult starts to tell the story or initiates a conversation with the child, reminding her or him what was said. Details are gradually checked with the child until she or he can talk about it directly.

Language

The importance of finding the words the child uses to describe bodily parts and functions has already been noted (p. 65).

Toys and play

Dolls' houses are useful, not least for ascertaining sleeping arrangements. Some children will provide revealing material through playing freely with dolls' houses, dolls (anatomically correct dolls are especially useful), or through drawing. Others respond to games which tell a story with, for example, glove puppets.

Adult responses

It is vital to convey to the child that she or he is believed, that the child has done nothing wrong and is not responsible for what has happened even if the sexual contact has been pleasurable. It is equally important not to display shock, horror, or disapproval if the child starts to talk freely.

Older children may ask what will happen, perhaps to their father, if they talk freely. After finding out what they have already been led to believe honest answers must be given, including the fact that they may be sent away from home or that their father may go to prison. This information creates a dilemma for the professional as well as for the child because of the need to keep her or his trust whilst, seemingly, betraying confidence.

Another difficulty is eliciting information from the child without implanting ideas. Leading questions such as 'Did your daddy do . . . ?' are not permissible but 'What did your daddy do?' is.

If a child is known to have been physically hurt through sexual experiences any further physical contact may seem like abuse. The professional should avoid touching the child in these circumstances although at other times this sort of physical contact is comforting and reassuring.

AFTER THE INTERVIEW

Where young people may appear as witnesses in criminal court proceedings, they need a great deal of support over long periods. A court appearance can be as traumatic as the sexual abuse itself. It can be helpful to prepare them for the experience by familiarizing them in advance with the court setting and procedures.

JANET AND HER GRANDMOTHER: AN INITIAL INTERVIEW

We describe below an initial interview with a five-year-old girl who had been sexually abused by a teenage boy who lived next door.

Janet, aged five, was referred to the psychiatric department in a children's hospital by the paediatrician in the hospital. Janet had been referred to him by a health visitor because she had been wetting herself in the day during the past twelve months although previously she had been dry.

There was a complicated social background: Janet's mother had not been able to look after her and had asked her own mother to take Janet, who now lived with her grandparents. It had recently been discovered that Janet had been sexually abused by Harry, a boy of about sixteen years old, a neighbour who used to play with Janet regularly. Janet and her family had had to move to London from another part of the country because of criticism by their neighbours. The health visitor learnt that the abuse had occurred on several occasions before anyone had taken proper notice of Janet saying that something sexual was going on with this boy. The family had talked very little about it before the consultation for Janet's daytime wetting. The paediatrician thought that the wetting was linked to the episodes of sexual abuse, which had included an attempt at intercourse, and referred Janet to the psychiatry department of the hospital.

Janet came to the interview with her grandmother, and also with the health visitor who had been an important support to the grandmother and to Janet since they had been in London. A male therapist conducted the interview.

Family and neighbours

Janet, aged 5.
Grandmother (maternal).
Harry, aged 16, and his younger brother John.

The interview

The therapist first established the relationship between Janet and her grandmother, and the fact that she did not live with her mother and father, using doll figures to represent different members of the family. The therapist then wanted to talk about the sexually abusive episodes. He asked Janet to go and sit on her grandmother's lap and continued to interview her.

Therapist (to grandmother): I want you to go over what happened with Janet. She can remember what happens and I think it would be very helpful if you could just help her to talk to you and tell you about it again.
Grandmother: She knows about it. [Then to Janet] You know when you lived in Wales?
Janet: No, I don't [taking the bottom of her dress which had slipped up her legs and pulling it firmly over her knees].
Grandmother: Yes you do. When you lived in Wales, who was your friend?
Janet: I don't know.

Grandmother: Who was it that helped you to speak? Who was John's brother?

Janet: Harry [covering up her knees even more firmly].

Grandmother: One day you were all playing and what happened?

Janet: I'm not going to tell you [quite crossly].

Therapist: Just remind her of what she told you and she will be able to talk to you about it.

Grandmother [covering up her mouth as she speaks]: Do you remember the day you asked me for talcum powder?

Janet: No, I don't remember.

Grandmother: Do you remember asking me for talcum powder?

Janet: I don't remember.

Grandmother: You were sore.

Janet: I don't know.

Grandmother: Of course you know. You told nanny and you told the police lady. Do you remember being in the police station and playing with typewriters and everything that was there?

Janet: No.

Therapist: Perhaps you could remind her what she told the police lady. I'm sure she will want to forget it but she does know it and it is better to talk about it, not to keep quiet.

Grandmother: You told the police lady. [Meanwhile grandmother was looking away from Janet and fiddling with her own coat.] You told the police lady that Harry put his . . . . [At this point Janet, who has been sitting with her back to her grandmother, turns around, takes her hand and puts it over her grandmother's mouth.]

Janet: It is rude!

Grandmother: I know it's rude, but this is a doctor.

Therapist: What word did she use?

Grandmother: She told the police lady that he put his willy in her polly.

Janet: [creasing up and putting her hand over her mouth, frozen and tense, trying again to put her hand over her grandmother's mouth]: It is rude.

Therapist: She came to tell you, is that right? [Grandmother agrees.] Did she know it was rude at that time, because she is a very big girl now, but did she know then? Does she know what willys and pollys are used for in grown-ups?

Grandmother [in a very soft voice]: Oh, just for weeing.

Therapist: But does she know about babies and how they are made?

Grandmother: No, she doesn't know how they are made. She doesn't know about that.

Meanwhile, Janet got off her grandmother's lap and crouched down by the table where the doll figures were, leaving the table between herself and the therapist. At the time of this interview, unfortunately, anatomically correct dolls were not available. This would have been the ideal time to use them, first to explore Janet's knowledge about the way that babies are born and conceived, using the dolls as mothers and fathers; then to show exactly what happened between Janet and the teenage boy who had sexually abused her; and then to show and talk about the relative sizes of herself as a child and the boy as a near adult. We had to make do with the small family figure dolls.

Therapist: Do you know actually that babies come out of the mummy's polly? [Therapist picks up the doll figure which represents Janet's biological mother and uses the baby doll to remind Janet that she had already told us that she had lived, first, 'in mummy's tummy and not in nanny's tummy and that mummy had in fact been born from nanny's tummy'.] You were doing it from your mummy's tummy so that you knew it came out. How do you think it came out? [Janet laughs in a very knowing way and grandmother interrupts.]
Grandmother: Well, Jennifer told you.

Janet actually knew much more about how babies were born than she could admit to. A great deal of information had been hidden (from consciousness) and it was not surprising that Janet had regressed and started wetting herself during the day.

Therapist [picking up Janet's giggling and laughing]: Well maybe you thought they came out of the mummy's bottom like a poos when you were little, and its only now you're big that you know how babies are really born. [Then to the grandmother.] So she came to tell you about this. Was she upset about this?
Grandmother: Well, it had happened three times before.
Therapist [echoing grandmother's words]: So it happened three times before?
Grandmother: She did say something but . . . .
Therapist: You did tell grandmother?
Grandmother: But I didn't believe her to tell you the truth.
Therapist: Nanny didn't believe you, she didn't think you were

telling the truth, she thought you were telling a big fib.
Grandmother: Yes.
Therapist [to grandmother]: How old is Harry?
Grandmother: He's sixteen.
Therapist: So he's very grown up.

Meanwhile, Janet has come around the table with the doll figures. She feels less anxious now that these matters are being spoken out aloud and feels free enough to bring the doll figures round the table to the therapist. She wants to show the therapist that she has picked out dolls representing herself and the boys.

Therapist: So, that one is Harry. He's really very big; and that is Janet and she is really very small. I suppose that Harry had a grown-up willy.
Janet [taking the clothes off the doll]: He hasn't got a willy.
Therapist: Well, he's a doll. I'm afraid that they don't often make dolls with willies. [Janet picks up the doll and throws it back into the box.]

Now that grandmother and the therapist were talking openly about what happened it seemed to give Janet permission to remember. Anatomically correct dolls would have been useful here. Children at this point in an interview, when encouraged to undress the dolls, will quickly show the therapist exactly what happened to them and will themselves mime and repeat these actions.

Therapist [to grandmother]: So, she told you three times.
Grandmother: But she didn't tell us much detail. It was only when she went up to my mother, her great grandmother, and gave her a kiss inside her mouth that we suddenly became very suspicious.
Therapist [to Janet, pointing out, with the dolls, the difference in size]: Harry is very big and you are very small. You will learn, when you are bigger, that grown-up men do put their willies inside the ladies' pollies to make a baby, but that Janet is much too little; she hasn't got breasts like her mummy has, and she is very small still, so that it's not right for her, as a little girl, to have that happen to her with Harry. [Trying to tell Janet about sexual intercourse so that she can understand that what has happened can be normal in other circumstances.]

Janet [to grandmother, picking up dolls and pushing them together]: Look [smiling], I've made them do it.

Janet is now free enough to be able to turn her experience from silence into play, to put this play activity into an appropriate context and understand it in terms of adult sexual activity. She is obviously very interested in this whole idea of being big and small. She takes the doll and puts it next to herself to try to explore this further. The therapist stands up by Janet to emphasize the difference in size between a grown-up (the therapist) and a little girl.

At this phase in the interview, Janet became very interested in the therapist, wanting to read his notes and stand near him, showing her affectionate feelings. This, of course, could easily be mis-read by adults as sexually provocative behaviour. The therapist, however, uses Janet's interest to re-emphasize the difference in size between Janet and Harry.

Therapist: You see, there's Janet, she was two and a half when this happened to her, and there's Harry, he was sixteen. So you can see how different they are from each other.

Janet then went on to do some drawings, she produced a symbolic figure, one that children who have been abused sexually often draw: a witch. This probably represents the child's experience of being hurt and punished.

This interview was the preliminary to a period of therapeutic work for Janet. She needed more information about sexual relationships at appropriate ages. Through individual and group therapy and play she had to learn how to protect herself from sexual abuse and how to avoid behaving in a way that might be seen as seductive. Another characteristic feature of this case was that although Harry's family at first condemned him they gradually became increasingly critical of Janet, seeing her as the bright child who had misled the older boy (he was rather dull). Janet and her grandmother and the whole family, therefore, had felt compelled to leave the area.

13 Initial case management[1]

There is widespread professional ignorance and denial concerning the emerging psychosocial problem of child sexual abuse. Even when cases are reported the consequences can still be devastating for the victim and the family. Break-up of the family whether through legal or therapeutic intervention is common and permanent emotional scars remain.

The 'battered child syndrome' was, in the main, first recognized by physicians, but sexual abuse rarely presents with objective clinical signs so that its discovery and the responsibility for management programmes of sexually abused victims and their families may best lie with social workers, family therapists, and other community workers. If child and family guidance clinics can overcome their traditional reluctance to work with 'unmotivated' families and are prepared to work within a legally prescribed framework, a valuable community resource is already available to develop therapeutic systems for intervention and consultation.

When the area review committee for child abuse in Northamptonshire decided to include in its child abuse register children in families where there was evidence of sexual abuse or exploitation, there was no reliable basis on which to estimate how many children were likely to be referred. However, it was possible to capitalize on the fact that agencies had developed relationships of trust while working with physical abuse, and a similar system of management for child sexual abuse was recommended and adopted.

During the four years of the study, eighty-one children were reported as victims and the proportion of sexually abused children reported to the register increased to 14 per cent of the total. It soon became clear that the management of these cases was time-consuming, complex, and demanding of the worker's personal resources. Consultation had to be readily available, and training schedules were rearranged to include work on problems relating to sexual abuse. By adopting a community-based response to child sexual abuse, the tasks of intervention, diagnosis, and long-term management were agreed on a multidisciplinary basis, and programmes for the treatment of individual family members, and later the whole family group, were developed to enable rehabilitation of the family where possible.

Johnson (1981) in an American study, concluded that public social agency workers do not generally provide, nor view the provision of, treatment services as primarily their responsiblity. Over 55 per cent of the cases of child sexual abuse in Johnson's study were referred to other agencies for treatment. In the UK, however, most child sexual abuse cases can and should be handled by existing child protective services – social services, child guidance clinics, and voluntary agencies – provided that adequate resources are available. The creation of further specialized units should be avoided but workers within existing organizations need special training for this work.

Another important problem is the effect of child sexual abuse on the workers themselves. Coming to terms with their own sexuality and potential to exploit can be stressful, and the worker's exposure to case material may unearth repressed and painful feelings.

It is valuable training for any professionals who deal with child sexual abuse cases to take part in small group sessions in which early traumatic sexual experiences can be recalled. About one-third of all social workers, male and female, disclose such events, their recollections remaining sharp and detailed even for events that occurred several decades ago.

This point is well illustrated by Henry Giarretto's (1981a) description of his first encounter with a family referred for father/daughter incest. He reported the interview with mother and daughter as going well – he listened to their confusion and pain and they left tearful but relieved. He set up an interview with the father. He writes:

> 'It was a particularly raunchy case, fondling at age five, oral copulation, and sodomy at eight, and full vaginal penetration at thirteen. A picture of the panic-stricken face of the girl I had just seen flashed in my brain. Instead of compassion, I was wracked by violent feelings towards the offender. I didn't want to listen to his side of the story, but to kick the bastard in the crotch instead.' (Giarretto 1981a: 8)

The disclosure of sexual abuse is still relatively rare and professionals are poorly prepared to deal with it; victims and family may therefore be deprived of therapeutic help at a time of crisis when they are most likely to benefit. Henry and Ruth Kempe have noted massive under-reporting. These authors write:

> 'It is understandable that the family resists disrupting the existing relationships: disclosure will result in public retri-bution, with the firm expectation of total family disruption, unemployment and economic disaster, loss of family and friends for the victim, and probably incarceration for the perpetrator at least until bail is stood. For each person involved there is also public shame of failure in his or her role as father, mother, and child, with further loss of self-esteem by all.'
> (Kempe and Kempe 1978: 62)

A heavy responsibility is placed on the professional to whom the disclosure is made. The victim wants the abuse to stop, the family members are subjected to close professional scrutiny, and invariably where there is prima facie evidence of sexual abuse, the police are involved. The perpetrator becomes the defendant within the court system; the victim becomes a witness, and the remaining parent and the rest of the family may not be given the chance for rehabilitation.

Rosenfeld and Newberger (1977) commented that in the 1960s child abuse was seen as an attack by a malicious adult against an unsuspecting child in need of protection. As we became more familiar with these adults, a more compassionate attitude towards them evolved. Professionals also developed intervention models aimed at helping all family members, not only the victimized child. Our 'discovery' of sexual abuse in the 1980s is in some ways similar but there are important differences. We can accept that many parents may, momentarily, lose physical control but it is difficult to persuade the public to feel any sympathy for parents who cannot control their sexual impulses towards children. The acceptable expressions of controlled sexual contact with children – breast-feeding, kissing, cuddling, and bathing, for example – seem to be unavailable to parents who sexually abuse their children.

About 85–90 per cent of perpetrators of sexual abuse are male and, as Finkelhor (1982) argues, this is an uncomfortable fact for many men to deal with. For this reason, and as men still occupy positions of administrative power, effective policies and public action may be hampered. Finkelhor concludes that as men begin to take more responsibility for the care of children they will become more concerned with children's well-being and will learn to enjoy affectionate relationships that have no sexual component, with the eventual result that more non-punitive policies will be developed.

Against a backcloth of agency procedures, legal requirements, and working relationships with the police, the social worker has to engage in a therapeutic relationship with all the members of the family – the victim, other children, the mother, and the perpetrator. The best interests of the children within the family are the social worker's primary concern but it is difficult to reconcile these interests with those of a society horrified by the nature of sexual abuse and demanding retribution. The legal processes are often incomprehensible to family members. The child will say: 'Why has daddy been taken away? Why can't I talk to him? It must be something terrible I've done.' Social workers are faced with a series of problems in managing child sexual abuse families. The perpetrator may strongly deny the abuse and unless there is clear forensic evidence it is difficult to proceed with action against him until he accepts the victim's allegations. Social workers have to believe the victim, and the

criteria on which they must base their interventions are conse-
quently wider than those required for evidence in law.

We recommend, as do many American authors (Giarretto
1981b), co-operation between the therapeutic and legal systems.

Pascoe (1979) argues that the overall aims of initial management of sexually abused children are:

(a) to care for the acute medical problems of the child;
(b) to care for the acute emotional problems of the child and
     family;
(c) to safeguard the child from further sexual abuse;
(d) to formulate plans for medical and psychological treatment
     for the child and family;
(e) to comply with legal requirements.

For the therapeutic team, the emphasis is on compassion and
sensitivity. The investigation team, police, social worker, and
doctor, should also first establish a working relationship with the
child.

Cooper (1978) recommends a gradation of legal and social
interventions, the choices depending on the severity and com-
plexity of the offence, using incarceration of the perpetrator only
as a last resort. In considering the alternatives it may be noted
that recidivism is rare when the family is properly handled at the
time of disclosure. With proper supervision the father can often
be kept in the community or even returned to his family.

Social workers undertaking child sexual abuse cases need
special training to enable open discussion with all family
members at the outset, a time when denial by the perpetrator can
be faced. The rules of evidence in the British legal system may
delay any opportunity the social worker has to discuss all the
issues. The result is usually that therapy with the father does not
take place and other family members are kept apart from him in
order to stop the incest. The victim becomes a 'treatment
hostage', kept in treatment against her or his will. If the
perpetrator is not included in the treatment programme the
chances of sexual abuse recurring are increased.

Social workers are accustomed to working closely with the
police in cases of physical abuse although the proportion of cases
the police investigate is small. NSPCC social workers, in common
with many of their local authority counterparts, are instructed
within their agency procedures to report, without delay, any

suspicion that a sexual offence has been committed against a child, whether or not the family is known to the social worker. The reasons for such an instruction are clear: (a) only the police are empowered within the present legal system to bring criminal proceedings for sexual offences, and (b) immediate forensic evidence is available to the police. The NSPCC recognizes that in families where sexual abuse of a child has occurred there is a need not only to provide support for the family as a whole, but also to assess whether legal protection is required for the abused child or other children within the family. Once a prima facie case of sexual abuse is established the matter should be referred to the police for investigation. For serious sexual offences the decision to prosecute is invariably based on advice from the DPP. Recommendations to the DPP, based on statements, professional opinions, the views of the case conference, and other evidence, can be made by the investigating team. The social worker is in a strong position to weigh up the effects of disclosure on the child and to assess risks if a family treatment plan is implemented.

Once a prosecution process is under way in the UK there is no turning back, unless the court so directs. It is, therefore, vital to concentrate on thorough assessment at the early stages in preparation for the initial case conference at which recommendations about future management are made.

At times, within the crisis of a referral and the consequent needs of adult family members, the social worker may deny or avoid the needs of the child. Sgroi (1975) has commented that recognition of sexual molestation in a child is entirely dependent on the individual's inherent willingness to entertain the possibility that the condition exists.

Summit (1983) has described the characteristic stages of a child's adaptation to sexual abuse within the family. Secrecy, helplessness, entrapment, and accommodation (to the existing situation), then delayed, conflicting, and unconvincing disclosure followed by retraction. This pattern will be recognized by anyone who has dealt with sexually abused children and does much to account for the common belief that many accusations come from childhood imagination or vindictiveness.

SYSTEM OF INTERVENTION IN CASES OF CHILD SEXUAL ABUSE

We now describe a stage-by-stage system of intervention for the management of these families. This system has been developed in Northamptonshire but seems sufficiently flexible to be used throughout the UK.

Stage 1

1 Once the sexual abuse is suspected, the case is referred to the police for investigation. Consultation is readily available for the referring worker through the resources at the NSPCC Special Unit. The unit is staffed by trained and experienced child abuse workers and supported by an adult psychiatrist, a child psychiatrist experienced in family therapy, a general practitioner/police surgeon, a clinical medical officer, and a paediatrician. Legal advice is also available. Other agencies may be asked to supply background information about the child and family.

2 The child victim, the mother, and, if appropriate, the alleged perpetrator are interviewed by police investigators who are accustomed to dealing with children and with family problems.

3 The social worker, particularly if he or she knows the family, is not only involved with the child and mother during the initial investigatory period but also with the perpetrator, acting as a link between them all (without betraying confidence). A place of safety order may have to be taken.

4 A physical examination is performed, usually by an experienced police surgeon. A female doctor is available for this examination if the victim wishes, for example if the family is Asian. The child's dignity and privacy are respected with the smallest possible number of people (two or three) present during the examination.

5 If there is corroborative evidence the perpetrator's separation from the family is usually recommended. An early appearance at the magistrates' court where the perpetrator is remanded either in custody or on conditional bail, ensures legal control. If the alleged offence is not corroborated the social worker must carefully consider the possibility that further abuse may occur if the alleged perpetrator returns home. Removal of the child and perhaps other children in the family may be necessary but must be arranged in such a way that the victim does not feel blamed for the family crisis. Such action requires

patience and skill, and emphasis is placed on the trust the child invests in the social worker.

6 If the social worker is satisfied that the child has been sexually abused and all the family members are motivated, a family meeting, carefully managed by the key workers involved, can take place to ensure that the whole family is aware of the nature of the disclosure, the process of further investigations, and the necessity for co-operation in recommended assessment procedures. At the magistrate's court hearing, the social worker in agreed cases informs the magistrates that he or she wishes to convene periodic family meetings and asks for permission for this to be written into the conditions of bail.

7 Once the initial investigation has been completed by the police, and the social worker has collated a social history about the family, a case conference takes place, to share information from the various disciplines represented and make recommendations for future management. Key workers are appointed who will take direct responsibility for continuing work with the family and individual family members. For example, the social worker may assume responsibility for work with mother, victim, and other children, while a probation officer may work with the father. The probation officer starts to bring together the various findings of the assessment team, the social worker and other agencies and to prepare a report for the court at the final hearing.

Stage 2

The perpetrator and other family members are given the opportunity for a psychiatric assessment as part of the assessment process. Ideally, the perpetrator sees a psychiatrist experienced in forensic and adult work, while mother and children are examined by a psychiatrist experienced in dealing with children and families. Findings are shared and co-ordinated.

Stage 3

Case conferences are continued, whether the case goes to court or not. The social worker arranges these meetings. A corporate plan, agreed with family members and based on family and individual needs, evolves.

Experience so far has shown that perpetrators are more likely to co-operate within legal sanctions. It is not generally realized that they usually find the therapeutic process more painful than punishment.

Stage 4

If the family co-operates and is thought to have the potential for change, the findings and recommendations are placed before the court. No attempt is made before sentence to force the parents to co-operate in treatment although the options can properly be spelt out. It may be necessary for social workers involved to give evidence in court.

Care proceedings should be seriously considered by the case conference; experience has shown that these families frequently change direction, easily slipping back into negative and destructive behaviour. A statutory order, that is, a care or supervision order, can help to avoid this, giving support to reliable long-term planning. Care proceedings can be used effectively without other legal measures.

NOTE

1 This chapter is based on the work of the National Society for the Prevention of Cruelty to Children (NSPCC) Special Unit and Family Centre in Northamptonshire, carried out between January 1979 and January 1983, and particularly emphasizes the part played by the social worker.

14 Organization of long-term family treatment

Although family-oriented work is thought to be the most appropriate treatment for sexually abused children and their families, this does not mean that all therapeutic meetings have to involve the whole family. It may be appropriate and is sometimes inevitable that different family members, or subgroups, are seen separately. For example, the social worker may work with the child, the probation officer with the father and a third professional with the mother. Work with individuals can be integrated with the work with the family through close cooperation between the different professionals involved.

Professionals should be open about the information they hold as far as it is relevant to the therapeutic process. Confidentiality between family members has also to be respected, and permission asked for before important issues are disclosed in joint meetings. It may be easier for individual family members to talk about difficult issues in family meetings when a number of professionals are present. The family process can be kept in mind at the same time as confidentiality towards individuals is maintained. It may be decided at a family meeting not to disclose a specific issue about one family member, an action that can be constructive for the family by defining necessary boundaries between individuals. Two or more family members may try to keep secrets from the rest but this need not be destructive provided the professionals realize what is happening.

THE CONJOINT FAMILY MEETING

In child sexual abuse, interventions can either have disastrous effects or be highly therapeutic. The first and central therapeutic step is to establish that each family member does actually know what has happened. The highest priority in any therapeutic strategy is to bring all family members to at least one or two conjoint meetings.

Aims of family meetings

1 To establish the facts about the sexual abuse. This is often forgotten or actively avoided. Each family member may have made separate statements to a variety of professionals. The statements may be long and it may have taken days to collect them. Professionals from different agencies may have talked at length about the facts of the abuse and also exchanged long written reports. The father may have pleaded guilty in court. The case may have reached the newspapers. Despite all these activities, within the family the fact of the incest may still be a secret. It has not been talked about openly by the persons most concerned − father, mother, and the children directly involved. Finally, the molested child may have indicated that abuse was occurring, even telling her or his mother or another member of the family, yet nobody may have acknowledged or believed the child's story. In the family meeting, no fact should be taken to be known, particularly the fact of the abuse itself.

The family meeting has first to establish the fact and circumstances of the sexual abuse, where it took place, and where everybody else was at the time. The use of unambiguous words (e.g. 'sexual relationship') may help the family to find an approach to a subject for which they may not have language. It is often unnecessary to discuss anatomical details about the sexual act itself; simple expressions – 'sexual intercourse' or 'putting the penis into the child' may be sufficient. The aim is to establish the facts clearly in a non-persecuting and emotionally neutral atmosphere.

2 To help the father to accept sole responsibility for the sexual act in the presence of the mother and other members of the family; this clearly takes any responsibility for what has happened away from the child. The father's responsibility must be explicitly articulated so that the children do not take the blame.

3 To help both parents come to an agreement about their joint responsibility for the care of their children. The most caring action that a father can take may be to agree to move out of the home and give up daily care of the child. The most caring thing that a mother can do may be to agree to postpone a decision about divorce, so that the children have time to come to terms with what has happened.

4 To talk openly about separations in the family, making sure that the therapeutic implications are understood. Even if there is no legal requirement for separation temporary partings at least are likely to occur during therapy in the face of the intense feelings that develop. The parents may wish to separate or a child may not want to return home. If the father leaves home it has to be made clear to the child and her or his siblings that they are not to blame. If a child leaves she or he should not be made to feel that no one in the family wants them to stay or that the separation is a punishment either for the abuse or for the problems arising from disclosure.

5 To set up a therapeutic contract about the extent of contact between the various members of the family and about visiting arrangements where family members are separated. The contract should also define clearly the ways in which the different professionals will be involved and the possible long-term plans for the family.

We have described the five aims of the conjoint family meeting in detail because of their fundamental therapeutic effects at the time and later.

It may not be possible to have an early family meeting. The father may have been arrested or the child may have been removed from the family. The family, especially the father, may refuse to co-operate. Even if the first family meeting cannot take place until years after the event, for example when the father comes out of prison, it should still be held and can still be worthwhile.

The children

The family meeting may lead into more structured family therapy but if this is not possible it is important that at least the child involved has somebody to talk to. Group work with two or more girls, or boys, can be useful and can help these children to speak more assertively at family meetings. They meet other children with similar experiences and their feelings of isolation, dirtiness, and worthlessness, turn out not to be unique. Group work can increase self-esteem and, through sharing the embarrassing, painful, but also powerful, feelings connected with their experiences of sexual activity with an adult, these children are able to develop confidence in themselves. Individual help may be needed when a child is grossly disturbed or for the practical reason that a suitable group does not exist in the area.

The parents

Some therapy, with both parents if the father is available or with the mother only when he is in prison, is always necessary. Even if regular sessions are not available locally contact with the parent must be built up or work with the child will break down. Changes in the child that derive from therapy cannot be integrated into the family setting without help for both parents, who may, for example, feel threatened by the changes that are occurring and forbid the child to continue treatment.

The child away from home

If the child is separated from the family, therapy must be established so that she or he does not feel abandoned. If the child moves into a children's home or into a family with other children the professionals involved in the child's primary treatment may have to agree on a cover story. They will affirm the story but one key person who knows about the abuse must be available so that the child has the opportunity to speak openly when she or he feels ready or needs to.

Siblings

These are important but easily forgotten. Contacts between siblings and the child concerned, and also between her or his close friends, must be maintained. Social contacts should be continued, if possible, although there is a danger that parents and friends may try to recreate the previous patterns of denial and secrecy in their meetings with children.

The mother

A wife whose husband is in prison may find herself suddenly not only without a partner but also without a wage-earner. She may respond by blaming the child for disclosing the sexual abuse. She may turn against her daughter, ally herself with the husband in prison, and oust the girl from the family. This leaves the child in an appalling situation. She has lost both parents, is blamed for the abuse, separated from siblings, and looked on as the odd one out amongst her friends.

The father

It becomes increasingly urgent to develop ways of helping the fathers while they are in custody. In prison a man may be prepared to work with the problem. When he comes out of prison and moves back with his wife, both parents may want to forget, feeling that the 'crime' has now been paid for. The sexually abused child in these families remains in danger. In the eyes of society and the law the father has paid for the crime; and there is no way to help the girl without parental agreement. At this stage the original victim or another child in the family may become involved in the abuse. If the parents are divorced, the man may start to molest another child in an alternative family. If direct help in prison through family meetings has not been possible, a meeting should be arranged by the local professionals, usually the social workers and the probation officer, a few weeks before the man's discharge. Prison governors and medical staff are increasingly co-operative over these meetings. If even this is not possible, a family meeting should take place the day the father comes out of prison. A father's release creates a crisis and it may be possible to engage the family in therapeutic work at this time. The chance will probably be lost when the father becomes accustomed to his released state. As well as the family meeting the father may also need individual or group psychotherapy.

THE PROFESSIONALS' WORK

As already noted, the further plan for each particular family depends on the specific needs of the family at the time of referral and on the availability and organization of professional help. The key professionals at this stage are the social worker and the probation officer. They may have both statutory and therapeutic obligations and there is a danger of these conflicting. Conflict can usually be avoided provided the professionals are clear about their statutory obligations. It is usually appropriate for the social worker to deal with the child or children and the probation officer with the father, but family meetings should also be held at intervals.

Professionals may find that they are being pressurized by the family into taking sides. This is generally a reflection of the family conflicts. A mother's needs and those of her child are likely to be different and the social worker who is dealing with the mother and daughter may be drawn into the conflict between them, or may be persuaded to join the mother and daughter in an alliance against the father. These problems can usually be solved by including other professionals in the treatment plan. For example, the family doctor is co-opted to work with the child while the social worker continues to work with the mother; or a marriage guidance counsellor could work with the mother whilst the social worker talks to the child; or a child guidance counsellor could talk to the child whilst the social worker keeps contact with the mother. More than three key professional figures probably should not be involved with any one family; close co-operation and quick feedback are necessary or the different agencies may be split by the family and drawn into the family conflicts.

CONCLUSION

Well-defined aims and co-operation between the professional agencies are needed in long-term treatment for the families in which a child has been sexually abused. We would like to emphasize three necessary ingredients for successful treament:

1 The family meeting.
2 Agreement amongst professionals on the treatment plan.
3 Therapeutic work with the family as well as with the child who has been abused.

15 The roles of professionals

This chapter summarizes the ways in which the various professionals may become involved with cases of child sexual abuse and outlines the actions professionals should take. Whatever actions they take, their primary obligation is to protect the child.

THE TEACHER AND YOUTH WORKER

Teachers and youth workers have a particular importance in child sexual abuse cases, because their regular contact with a child over a long period enables them to observe changes in mood or behaviour. These changes are often the result of stresses at home, one of which may be sexual abuse. Victims of sexual abuse often report that they feel distanced from their friends because they have entered the adult sexual world whilst their friends remain 'little girls'. Sudden isolation from peers may also serve as an indicator of sexual abuse. Teachers and youth workers may also be able to observe the interaction between parent and child.

Affection and tenderness are essential to a child's healthy emotional development, but workers will be intuitively aware when the physical contact they observe proceeds beyond what is normal and nurturing and becomes essentially sexual. Children often dress up in adult clothing as part of a process of experimentation with adult roles, just as from time to time they are curious about each other's bodies. Abnormal preoccupation with sexual matters suggests either that sexuality is a dominant feature of family life, or that the child is learning that the way to function effectively is to behave in a sexual manner.

Suspicion that a child is being sexually abused, even without corroboration, should be reported to the social services department. The social worker will then arrange the necessary interviews and a case conference. Even if suspicions are not confirmed, the family may still need help.

If a child alleges sexual abuse it is important that the teacher or youth worker does not magnify the damage to the child either by reacting in an emotional, judgemental way, or by disbelieving the story. It is crucial that subsequent help for the child is not impeded by careless handling at this stage. The worker should ask only questions that will help the child to talk, and should reassure her or him that what is said is being taken seriously. Careful notes, verbatim if possible, should be written after the interview. If the alleged perpetrator is an immediate family member the child should not be allowed home until the worker receives further instructions from her or his own supervisor, the social services, or the NSPCC.

By choosing to make an allegation to the teacher or youth worker, the child has demonstrated considerable trust in that person. Investigations are bound to be acutely embarrassing for the child, both physically and emotionally, and the worker's support through these processes is invaluable. The school can give practical help, for example by rearranging lessons so that the teacher concerned can provide the child with this support.

THE SOCIAL WORKER

The social worker's primary task is to protect the child. For this task, social workers are authorized to ensure that all allegations of child abuse are thoroughly investigated. Procedures are agreed on a multidisciplinary basis through area review committees for child abuse; thus the professionals' and the employing agency's views are included, and overlap and conflict are avoided.

The social worker is in a key position and is usually responsible for checking with other agencies for information about referred children and their families and, once the investigation has been completed, for ensuring that a case conference is convened. In all these tasks, the social worker's responsibility is to work closely with other professionals. The social worker, supervised by a senior colleague, relates to the needs and protection of the child and, in accordance with local procedures, arranges for medical examination and consultation. Where a prima facie case of sexual abuse is established, the social worker also, through his contract of employment, has to inform the police.

During the initial stages of referral, the social worker relates to children and parents in a number of ways:

1 by answering questions and supplying information;
2 by allowing anxieties and stresses felt by the parents to be voiced;
3 by gathering comprehensive background information – the social history – from which a base for assessment and future work is established.

COUMMUNITY CHILD HEALTH SERVICE WORKERS: CLINICAL MEDICAL OFFICER, HEALTH VISITOR, SCHOOL NURSE

The clinical medical officer working in a child health clinic, day nursery, or school may well be the first person to recognize child sexual abuse, either as the result of disclosures by parent or child, or because of suspicions aroused whilst seeing the child. Unless the child needs immediate referral to hospital because of trauma, there will always be time to listen to the relevant history. The extent of the physical examination will vary but should never include more than an inspection of the genital region and anus. Every effort should be made to avoid subjecting the child to repeated examinations. If, therefore, there is a chance that sexual activity has occurred within the previous forty-eight hours the child should be referred for fuller examination. The clinical medical officer who suspects that a child has been sexually abused should discuss the case with a senior officer who is familiar with local services and procedures for the investigation of such cases. The overriding consideration is the protection of the child. This may require admission to hospital under the care of a paediatrician. The social services department should be informed so that arrangements may be made for a case conference.

When health visitors or school nurses have reason to suspect sexual abuse of a child they should first inform the nursing officer. A discussion can then take place immediately between the health visitor, clinical medical officer, and/or the general practitioner and arrangements for assessment and investigation can be made.

THE GENERAL PRACTITIONER

A general practitioner should always be alert to the possibility of child sexual abuse and consider it in the differential diagnosis of children who present with any of the indicators described above (pp. 5–8).

A detailed history and family history are taken and a general medical examination carried out. The examination must include inspection of the genital region and anus but any further examination should be delayed until the child can be seen by a doctor who is familiar with the procedures for investigation of sexual abuse, for example a police surgeon or a paediatrician. If there is a possibility that sexual abuse has occurred during the previous forty-eight hours this further examination with the collection of forensic specimens must be arranged immediately. The child should not be washed and the clothing must not be removed.

The general practitioner may already know the child. If the doctor can carry out the examination sensitively, allowing time for talking, it can be a good opportunity for learning more from the child about what has happened.

In the non-urgent case where sexual abuse is not suspected within the previous forty-eight hours, the child should be treated as a case of non-accidental injury and referred to hospital for admission and investigation by the hospital paediatrician. If hospital admission is not indicated but sexual abuse is suspected, discussions with other professionals, not only the other members of the primary care team but also senior social workers, consultant paediatricians, the police surgeon, school teachers, and non-professionals, will be necessary.

The general practitioner must not act alone. Ideally, an early case conference of key workers is convened and the established procedures for non-accidental injury followed. The temptation for general practitioners to act alone will not be so great if local resources for follow-up and treatment of the whole family unit are seen to be effective. Because of the contractual obligation of social services to report to the police and the consequent necessity for early police investigation, many general practitioners are reluctant to divulge information about cases they suspect in their own practice. This is never justified because of the risk of further incidents of abuse to the child and other children in the family. Therapeutic measures can only work within the legal framework.

THE POLICE SURGEON

The police surgeon should be competent in clinical forensic medicine (preferably, in the UK, holding the Diploma in Medical Jurisprudence) so that he or she is not only able to collect necessary evidence but is also experienced in the legal aspects of child sexual abuse, is familiar with court procedures, and can withstand cross-examination. The police surgeon is often required to examine a possible sexual abuse victim and should, therefore, be especially sensitive to the needs of the victim. The sex of the individual who does the medical examination is less important than his or her competence and sensitivity. Fortunately, most police surgeons are family doctors in active practice dealing with women and children every working day.

The medical examination in cases of alleged or reported child sexual abuse should always take place in a clinical setting. Local circumstances vary but the most suitable place for the examination may be the doctor's surgery or the local hospital. In non-urgent cases the police surgeon will arrange a time and place of examination to suit the victim, even the child's home if necessary, so that investigative procedures cause as little disruption as possible.

In some areas the police surgeons have delegated responsibility in this field to another group, for example the local paediatric unit, or to specially formed groups of doctors (usually female) who deal with medical aspects of all sexual offences against women and children.

The overriding principle is that *the medical examination should be carried out in a proper clinical setting*, where one would be prepared for a member of one's own family to be examined.

Successful co-operation can be established by the police surgeon, acting as a medical liaison officer, between the police on the one side and the medical profession and social services on the other. An experienced police surgeon, accepted by fellow general practitioners, hospital doctors, and social workers, as well as the local senior police officers, can do a great deal to promote liaison between the various professionals and the police, for example by arranging with the hospital paediatrician urgent admission for a child requiring examination under anaesthetic. Medical colleagues can discuss confidential matters with the police surgeon on a doctor-to-doctor basis and can rely on professional discretion as to the information that is transmitted to other agencies, especially the police.

THE HOSPITAL PAEDIATRICIAN

There are several ways in which the hospital paediatrician may become involved with suspected cases of child sexual abuse.

1 The child may be brought to the hospital by a parent, social worker, police officer, or some other adult making an allegation of sexual abuse.
2 The child may be referred by a general practitioner or other doctor with a suspicion of sexual abuse.
3 The paediatrician may suspect sexual abuse in the course of a routine consultation or the child or parents may report sexual abuse in confidence.

Allegation of sexual abuse

In the case of an allegation of sexual abuse staff in the accident and emergency department should call the most senior member of the paediatric medical staff on duty. When only junior staff are available the consultant should be informed immediately and will give further instructions. If there are genital injuries an experienced surgeon should be called to give treatment and collect forensic specimens.

The first task of the paediatrician is to ascertain the facts from those concerned, in a suitable private room and in the presence of a witness. Gentleness and an unhurried approach are necessary. A young child must be helped to tell the story through doll play or drawing and someone the child knows and trusts should be present. Then, after careful explanation, the child should be medically examined with inspection of the genital region and anus. The paediatrician then decides whether or not there are grounds for continuing suspicion. Where there are none the child may be allowed to return home but further investigation of the family may be necessary. But if suspicion remains the child should probably be admitted to hospital for further investigation and the collection of forensic specimens. Sometimes a stay with a relative or admission to a children's home will be appropriate.

At this stage the local child abuse team, if there is one, can be brought in and a case conference will be arranged for a few days ahead when the preliminary medical and social investigations are completed. Assistance from a child psychiatrist or clinical psychologist may be sought at this time.

In all cases accurate detailed notes must be made as these will form the basis for written reports and evidence that may have to be given in subsequent legal proceedings in juvenile courts, the High Court and, rarely, the criminal court. It is useful to quote verbatim the essential features of the child's story. Attitudes of family members towards the child, and the child's relationship with the parents and other relations, should be noted. It is important to check what becomes of the child, sometimes through other professionals rather than directly, to ensure that protection against further abuse is combined with therapy designed to help her or him to understand what has happened and to resolve the resulting emotional trauma.

Referral by another doctor

When the child is referred by another doctor background information should be obtained from the doctor and from any other professional workers already in contact with the family. The child's symptoms should be discussed with the parents while taking a general medical and family history. Sometimes a parent may hint at sexual matters; with a little help and sympathy worries may be revealed. Seeing the parents separately may help but involved fathers often prefer to remain in the background, hoping for continued secrecy.

The child should be seen alone and, in private, may make allusions to sexual activity. If these are probed with sympathy and patience the history of sexual abuse may be revealed. The child should be reassured that it is right to tell, that she or he is not to blame and that the doctor wants to help the adult to stop the activity. The physical examination then proceeds as described. If, as a result of the history and examination, the paediatrician confirms that sexual abuse may be occurring, this must be discussed with the parents. The process of further investigation must be explained and a case conference arranged.

In the other situations in which the paediatrician comes to hear of possible or actual sexual abuse the investigation proceeds in a similar way with modifications to suit individual circumstances.

CHILD GUIDANCE PERSONNEL

Child guidance personnel may be directly involved in diagnosing sexual abuse in children referred for other reasons. Their primary task is the protection of the child. It may become apparent during a diagnostic assessment that a child referred because of physical or behavioural problems has been or is being sexually abused. In the latter case action must be initiated to protect the child, through liaison with social services; this may necessitate providing reports or giving evidence in care or criminal proceedings. Sexual abuse may emerge in the background of one of the parents either in the course of social history taking or during treatment. Sexual abuse may come to notice in the course of consultations with schools, day nurseries or family centres, or with general practitioners, either through expressed concern about or actual observation of a particular child.

Child guidance personnel are usually not in the front line. They are rarely involved at the time of disclosure of child sexual abuse, in investigation of allegations, or in immediate crisis management but are more likely to be used by other agencies, for example health and social services, as follows:

1 Consultation for professionals unsure of how to proceed in

the light of suspicions or allegations of child sexual abuse, particularly where there is difficulty or conflict.

2 Assistance in conducting the family meeting after disclosure, with the aim of discussing the facts in the presence of family members.

3 Assessment of children known or suspected to have been sexually abused and provision of reports on a child's emotional state, development, intellectual abilities, and behaviour. Siblings and parents should be seen as part of this assessment.

4 Long-term treatment, including individual psychotherapy for the child, case work with mothers whose partners have been removed, and marital or family therapy.

Child guidance personnel are in a strong or sometimes the key position to offer treatment to children and their families when sexual abuse has occurred (especially if they are not involved in the exercise of statutory powers) and to give support to other professionals. They are experienced in working with children in the age range in which sexual abuse usually presents (11–15 years) and have the skills to help such children.

THE CHILD PSYCHIATRIST

A child psychiatrist is involved with sexually abused children and their families in several different ways.

1 The issue of sexual abuse may arise during the assessment of any clinical problem, either during the history-taking, family interview, or during psychiatric examination or treatment. The psychiatrist's understanding of emotional symptoms and disturbed behaviour will alert him or her to the possibility that these are manifestations of sexual abuse and of the child's attempts to cope with the problem.

2 A child and family may be referred directly in order for the psychiatrist to confirm the occurrence or extent of alleged sexual abuse; whether the act did in fact take place or whether it is part of a child's fantasy, a distorted perception or deliberate distortion of events. Deeper involvement with the family may result and progress to longer-term management including individual psychotherapy with the child.

3 The psychiatrist may be asked to take the role of the child's

advocate so as to ensure safety and the opportunity for normal emotional and social development within the family of origin or in substitute care. The psychiatrist may be asked to appear in court as an expert witness to testify to the child's emotional state and competence and to make recommendations to meet the long-term needs of child and family.

4 Psychiatrists working in consultation with paediatricians or social workers bring their particular knowledge to multidisciplinary assessments and interventions; they may help to establish the facts where abuse is suspected or to supervise the work of others more directly concerned with child and family.

5 The child psychiatrist teaches medical and nursing staff on paediatric wards and sometimes general wards, resident staff in children's homes, foster parents, and other substitute caretakers. Background information about the origins of sexual abuse and associated psychopathology in involved individuals, the implications of isolated incidents as against prolonged abuse, and issues of family loyalty, family structure, and family relationships, are necessary knowledge for those who deal with these cases.

THE GENERAL PSYCHIATRIST

The general psychiatrist may become involved in the management of child sexual abuse through a particular interest in the problems of the family or in the treatment of adult perpetrators and other family members. The general psychiatrist is rarely the first contact but may be involved as a consultant or through service to distressed patients.

Family members, social workers, nurses, or others who become aware of sexual abuse within a family may seek the advice of a psychiatrist either on their management of the family or with a view to securing treatment for the perpetrator. The protection of the child must always be paramount and if advice to ensure this is not accepted (the individuals seeking advice are often upset and may fail to observe their normal practices) it may be necessary to take independent action. In most cases this means that this person should consult with the local paediatrician or report the case to the NSPCC or to the area director of social services.

The psychiatrist is most commonly involved through his or her contact with distressed patients. A mother or a young girl recovering from a drug overdose may reveal a story of sexual abuse. A depressed and guilty perpetrator may seek help. The psychiatrist, however, must be aware of the possibility of the false confessions of a psychotic patient and the danger of over-reacting to these. Requests for termination of pregnancy, depression during pregnancy or after delivery, and sexual problems including promiscuity may all lead to the disclosure of continuing sexual abuse.

Not uncommonly guilt, shame, or anger over long past sexual abuse emerges in patients during treatment for other psychiatric disabilities. There is little point in confronting an old man with events that took place twenty or thirty years previously but it is always necessary to establish that his daughters' children are not being interfered with, either by their father or their grandfather (the patient himself).

Whenever the psychiatrist identifies continuing abuse there is an immediate responsibility to protect the present child victim. If possible the psychiatrist's actions should be with the consent of the patient but it may be necessary, in the case of a child at risk, to breach confidentiality without this consent (see also pp. 52–5).

THE FORENSIC PSYCHIATRIST

The forensic psychiatrist is a general psychiatrist with a special experience of psychiatry in relation to the law. All that has been written for general psychiatrists applies to their forensic colleagues.

In addition, the forensic psychiatrist is more likely to be consulted in those cases where prosecution is pending or the perpetrator has been sentenced. The defence or prosecution may request a report relating to the individual's state of mind at the time of the offence, to impairment of responsibility, to mitigating circumstances, or to the possibility of a treatment order under the Mental Health Act (1983) or a condition of treatment order under the Powers of Criminal Courts Act (1973). The forensic psychiatrist's primary concern is with the accused and the judicial process, not with the victim and family.

Whenever possible the psychiatrist should seek to contact the group responsible for the care of the victim. Ideally, a pooling of information will then occur and the court can be offered guidance on the relative implications, for the victim and family, of a custodial or non-custodial sentence, and on the prospects of rehabilitation.

This ideal is not achieved: in practice, the prosecution may request access to information to obtain further support for its case and the defence lawyers may prohibit releasing the information lest it weaken theirs. It may be possible to find other means of sharing information, for example a case conference after the verdict but before sentence, but the judge may be reluctant to accede to this.

Where the forensic psychiatrist is consulted by client, probation officer, social worker, general practitioner, or any other colleague about a case that has not come to the attention of the law, his options and responsibilities are those of the general psychiatrist.

THE POLICE OFFICER

If a child mentions abusive sexual activity to a police officer, the officer encourages her or him, tactfully and unemotionally, to continue the account of the act and circumstances. It is not advisable to move to a specially quiet or private place or to call a witness, as this may silence the child. The police officer should record what has been said immediately after the 'interview', using the child's own words if possible. The officer should also see that arrangements are being made for the medical examination. The next task for the police officer is to investigate the case.

In criminal matters arising from child sexual abuse the statutory duty to investigate falls mainly on the police and they initiate any prosecution. This does not absolve them from recognizing that such abuse is an emotive subject and that each case will raise complex issues that can only be resolved by close co-operation with other agencies. All police officers will be aware of this and will accept that the interests of the child are paramount.

The police, because of their experience and training in investigation, are the best people to elicit the facts, but they accept the need for close co-operation with other agencies before final decisions are made, except in those serious cases that require immediate decisions (for details see pp. 37–9).

There is nothing to stop the police officer from drawing the attention of the DPP or other prosecuting authority to the views of workers in other agencies; this assists in making decisions about future management. Even in sexual abuse cases there are many occasions when a prosecution is neither desirable nor prudent (see pp. 39–40).

THE PROBATION OFFICER

Traditionally the work of the probation service, through its officers, is to serve the courts, both criminal and civil. The primary duties of the probation officer in both settings are, therefore, the provision of reports giving information and recommendations as requested by the court, and supervision of those placed under appropriate orders by the court, ensuring that any special requirements contained in those orders are enforced.

In the past two decades probation officers have also provided a wider range of services for the containment and rehabilitation of offenders in the community, including a social work service in penal establishments that continues after the prisoners' release; this after care service is compulsory for those released on licence or parole and voluntary for others. The probation officer's help may be needed at three stages:

1 where there is suspicion or complaint with regard to an existing client or that client's family;
2 at the sentencing stage;
3 in prison and on release.

As with the other professionals involved in the management of child sexual abuse families, action to safeguard the child is accepted as vital.

Suspicion or complaint

At the first sign of suspicion or complaint the probation officer acts in accordance with agreed local procedures, working closely with the local area health authority on whose child abuse committee the chief probation officer sits or is represented. The probation officer attends the initial and subsequent case conferences and participates in the work of these conferences until the end of the statutory responsibility for the client. The probation officer identifies the work she or he will undertake and contracts with the case conference to do this work.

The sentencing stage

At this point, following a guilty plea or a finding of guilt, a social enquiry report is provided for the court. Whilst the primary purpose of this report is to inform the court of the social circumstances of the offender, it is accepted practice that a sentencing recommendation is made. This report could be the vehicle for recommending work with the offender using resources within the community. A probation order with special requirements, for example residing only where approved by the probation officer or submission to treatment under the direction of an experienced medical practitioner, may be needed. Such requirements can extend for the whole period of the probation order or for a lesser, specified, period. Before making the order for medical treatment, a court must be satisfied, on the evidence of a medical practitioner approved for the purposes of section 12(2) of the Mental Health Act 1983, that the offender needs and may respond to treatment. As the offender has to agree to be placed on probation and to all conditions of the order, he must fully understand what is expected of him (see p. 47)

Care in prison and on release

In this area of intervention the probation officer assumes responsibility for care in prison and after care on release for all those sentenced to imprisonment; where there is early release the period of licence is supervised by a probation officer. When a prisoner is released at the end of the sentence he is entitled to the help of the probation service but supervision cannot be enforced by the probation officer. However, combination of the work of the probation officers in the prison and those in the local area can often ensure a constructive approach, including attendance of the offender at case conferences. The (usually) father's involvement at the case conference can be used either as part of a therapeutic plan for the family or, where necessary, for steering him away from the family following his release. In all cases where prisoners have been convicted of sexual offences against children in the home, the prison department has to draw the attention of local authorities to the fact that the prisoner is being released. This responsibility is delegated to the probation officer working in prison, and directors of social services now have guidance as to what action they should take (DHSS/Welsh Office 1978).

Part Four: Prevention

16 Prevention and education

Child sexual abuse is a major public health problem that needs a preventive approach. This involves alerting children, parents, and professionals to the problem and providing children with information and the basic skills necessary for their safety and well-being.

In the past three years television and radio, and newspapers and magazines, have mostly tackled the problem thoughtfully and sensitively. This has had an impact on the adult population leading to an increasing number of reported cases, but most of these media efforts have not been devised for, nor have they reached, children.

Finkelhor (1982), in his Family Violence Research Program at the University of New Hampshire, describes what parents tell (or do not tell) their children about sexual abuse. He underlines how often lack of knowledge, or uncertainty about normal behaviour, is a factor in a child's victimization. Children often say they were confused and misled by the abuser's insistence that the sexual activity was proper and normal; or that they did not know they had a right to refuse or that other adults would defend them if they complained; or that they were thrown off their guard when the adult behaved in a way that they had never been led to expect. One effective preventive measure, therefore, would be to see that the children themselves know more about sexual abuse.

Informed children, who are confident about situations and people and have some idea about where to get help if they need it, are less likely to become the victims of any type of assault. Yet most of our children do not have sufficient knowledge to resist sexual abuse and any information they do receive is often too late, inaccurate, misleading, and even frightening. Vague warnings about dangerous strangers who are out to 'get them' under various pretexts are not helpful.

Ideally, sex education should be a continuing process within the family; in reality, the family remains a powerful source of inhibition and misinformation and professionals must accept a substantial educational role for children and adults.

There are also many obstacles to discussing general sexual matters, let alone the topic of sexual abuse, in schools. Many teachers and educators believe the educational curriculum should not include sexual matters. In spite of these difficulties, schools seem to be amongst the most promising settings for introducing and developing educational projects designed to prevent child sexual abuse, and some impressive programmes have been undertaken in schools in North America and Canada (Brassard *et al.* 1983; Metropolitan Chairman's Special Committee in Child Abuse, Toronto 1980).

For school projects to be useful the support of the adults concerned is important. This means that parent–teacher associations must be involved, and small group sessions arranged for teachers and parents.

Facts about sexual abuse and discussion of appropriate and inappropriate touch are two subjects that have been found especially important in sex abuse preventive programmes for children in North America (Brassard *et al*, 1983). Theatrical productions and videos can be used to provide illustrations and the teacher should be supplied with appropriate teaching material.

The provision of information alone is not enough. In western societies most people have sexual inhibitions and anxieties that are rooted in their own past and influence their work with clients in the present. An embarrassed teacher or a doctor who retreats into clinical verbiage will inhibit rather than inform. In order to achieve self-confidence and ease in discussing sexual matters some means must be found to release inhibitions and acquire skills in talking about sexual intimacy. Small group discussions for professionals with an experienced leader can provide a safe environment for this purpose. The first adults who must be educated are the professionals themselves.

Children need to achieve a sense of autonomy over their own bodies and to develop appropriate standards of privacy and intimacy. Standards imposed from the outside may be unacceptable to normal families whose habitual practices will range from uninhibited nudity within the family to undressing only behind closed doors in private. Children must also acquire acceptable standards of social behaviour in which their need for privacy can be expressed and accepted. The differences between the delighted discoveries of nursery school: 'Mummy! Boys stand up when they pee,' the fumblings of adolescence, and the inappropriate interest of older people are best learned with other children. Secrecy needs to be differentiated from privacy and the hazards of any intimacy or violation of privacy, especially when surrounded by efforts at concealment or associated with injunctions or threats, or attempts to bribe, need to be explained. Above all openness should be encouraged; many children are still unable to ask questions or make comments about bodily functions in the presence of their parents or teachers.

Doctors and nurses should have some specialized knowledge. Social workers and teachers should have some general understanding of the biological and psychosocial basis of human sexuality and be able to discuss such topics when appropriate.

Once sexual abuse is suspected the professional involved must take steps to protect the child. No alleged perpetrator should be condemned out of hand but no child who even hints at sexual abuse should be left unsupported. It is important to avoid inappropriate or panicky over-reaction. Early confrontation is often associated with denial by the perpetrator and then retraction by the child.

PERSONAL SAFETY FOR CHILDREN

The adaptability of the human organism is such that a stable state can be achieved within a family in which sexual abuse is occurring even with persisting abuse. The victims develop behaviour for survival which, outside the incestuous family, is seriously maladaptive.

Such children need an opportunity in a secure and trusting environment to talk about their experience and to be reassured of their integrity and absolved of guilt or shame. They need training in social skills to change their precociously and unconsciously sexual body language, returning it to something more appropriate to their age group.

All children need to learn how to protect themselves. This is especially important for the victims of sexual abuse, for whom the risk of further abuse by other family members or friends is greatly increased. Children need to know of their exclusive rights over their own body, particularly their sexual or 'private' parts. They should know that even a parent, a doctor, or a nurse should only touch them with their permission and with a good reason, such as helping a young child to wash or inspecting an injury.

The child needs a language to describe the genitalia and sexual acts. This will vary according to age, social class, geographical area, and local factors. The words should not be so clinical as to be incomprehensible nor so vulgar as to attract opprobium. The pudendum is known as the fanny, cunt, pussy, polly, or love box in different parts of the UK, but to speak in these terms outside the locality of their common usage would cause amusement or distaste.

Once what is permissible, by whom and why, has been established, the child needs to know how to warn off predators or seek help. To pick up an exploring hand and say 'don't do that', to call someone else into the room, to hiss 'piss off', to walk away, or to tell a parent, teacher, doctor, or social worker are all appropriate responses in particular circumstances. The techniques for teaching self-protection must be geared to a child's circumstances and are probably best learned through role play in a group. Assertion training of a more general kind may in itself be effective, for many victims are selected because of their isolation and evident vulnerability.

PORNOGRAPHY AND THE MEDIA

Pornography

An extensive trade exists in photographs and videos of children in provocative poses or actually engaged in sexual activities. The children may be of any age from a few weeks old to adolescent. Although there is no reliable evidence on the role of pornography in child abuse, common sense suggests that these children are corrupted by the process and in even greater danger from those who permit it. On balance it is believed that the majority of viewers of pornography are uninfluenced by or achieve harmless sexual gratification from the experience. There is, however, a powerful suggestion that those whose sexual development is aberrant or immature may be unduly influenced by such exposure. McGuire *et al.* (1965) have demonstrated the powerful shaping of sexual response through fantasy. The risks of encouraging paedophilia and of harming the child participant seem sufficiently serious to condemn the production or showing of explicit sexual material involving children.

The media

The media can make an important contribution both with specifically educational programmes and through popular programmes. *The Archers* may be more influential than the school service of the BBC, and popular magazines for adolescents more effective than British Medical Association pamphlets. Unfortunately the theme of sex and violence pervades much of 'entertainment' and the broadcasting authorities must be kept under pressure to limit such material and restrict it to adult viewing times.

The increasing availability of video recorders and the availability of soft pornography or blue videos, which are regarded by many as light family entertainment, are inducing a dramatic change in the language and understanding of younger children as well as producing often inappropriate sexual arousal in family settings.

The setting of standards depends, ultimately, upon the family and it is to dysfunctional families that the greatest preventive action must be directed.

17 Self-help groups and alternative support networks

Self-help groups, volunteers, and others involved in providing alternative support play an important part in responding to the problem of child sexual abuse. Professionals in statutory and other agencies and volunteers and those involved in the self-help movement should continue to build up and maintain a trusting, flexible partnership. The two groups serve different purposes but at times their functions overlap and each should consult with and refer cases to the other, even though co-operation may be difficult for ideological, personal, and professional reasons.

Co-operation can take various forms. A strong self-help component, backed by support from professionals has worked well in several child sexual abuse treatment projects in the USA (Giarretto 1977). These programmes have aimed to co-ordinate legal processes and therapeutic intervention. The sexual abuse treatment project in progress at the Hospital for Sick Children, Great Ormond Street, London (see pp. 13–14), has also shown that a variety of groups, including self-help groups, are required to meet the needs of victims, perpetrators and others affected by the disclosure of sexual abuse. It is also evident that such groups can play an important part in the reunion and rehabilitation of families where this seems possible.

Self-help groups now exist for most of the different categories of individuals affected, directly or indirectly, by the sexual abuse of children. There are groups for recent victims of both sexes, organized according to age and development; for siblings of children who have been sexually abused; for perpetrators; for mothers whose children have been sexually abused; and for parents who wish to focus on their marital relationship.

As well as the self-help component in particular treatment projects backed by professionals, services run by volunteers and independent self-help groups are useful in their own right. Their special value is their ability to understand and respond to the stigma, guilt, and dread of exposure experienced by victims and perpetrators, their fear of police involvement and the consequences of legal intervention, and their desire to preserve anonymity whilst seeking advice and assistance.

There are few agencies where children can independently refer themselves. A direct access, twenty-four-hour telephone, or walk-in service for children would be valuable and could be organized by a voluntary group. There would be ethical problems for such a self-referring service for children, but the absence of such a service is a clear gap in the treatment programmes for child sexual abuse in the UK.

Existing self-help and alternative support groups are active in the following ways:

1 They increase the awareness and understanding of child sexual abuse through victims sharing their experience via the media and through the distribution of carefully produced information.

2 They run twenty-four-hour, 'hot-line' telephone services which provide information, advice, support, and confidential counselling for those affected by or concerned about child sexual abuse. Already such services are leading to the identification of many new cases.

3 They provide alternative counselling services for members of families in which child sexual abuse has recently occurred, and work to improve medical, legal, and social services for cases

that come to light through professional channels.
4 They put adult victims in touch with each other and help to set up other self-help groups.
5 They campaign for refuges for adult female victims of child sexual abuse.
6 They provide links with other similar services.

It is as difficult for the founders of self-help groups as it is for professionals to sustain effort in this emotionally taxing field. Voluntary groups are especially vulnerable to withdrawal of financial and other support. Telephone numbers change or telephones cease to operate as advertised, often due to sheer overload of calls received. The character and aims of a group may alter if key personnel withdraw. These changes make it difficult to compile a reliable list of permanent resources. The groups listed below are less impermanent than most. In addition, we suggest readers contact their Citizens' Advice Bureau or Health Centre, addresses for which may be found in telephone directories. The alternative press often contains information about self-help groups and may give advice on the telephone.

RESOURCE GROUPS

Capital Helpline
London
Tel 01 388 7575
Weekdays 9.30–17.30

Incest Crisis Line
Richard
Tel 01 422 5100
Shirley
Tel 01 890 4732

Incest Survivors Campaign
c/o AWP Hungerford House
Victoria Embankment
London WC2
Tel 01 836 6081

Mothers of Abused Children
Chris Strickland
Tel 0965 31432

OPUS (Organisations for
        Parents under Stress)
Contact: Information Officer
26 Manor Drive
Pickering
Yorkshire YO18 8DD

Altrincham
Tel 061 941 4011/4012

Amersham
Tel 0494 715050

Belfast
Tel 0232 238800

Birmingham
Tel 021 440 5444

Borehamwood
Tel 01 207 2751

Cambridge
Tel 0480 216136

County Durham
Tel 0388 766826

Crawley
Tel 0293 519550

Croydon
Tel 01 668 4805

Doncaster
Tel 0302 28668

Leicester
Tel 0533 886735

Lichfield
Tel 05432 54341

London
Tel 01 263 8918

Malvern
Tel 068 45 68228

Milton Keynes
Tel 0908 678877

Newcastle upon Tyne
Tel 0632 28168

Nottingham
Tel 0602 624499

Oxford
Tel 0865 726600

Peterborough
Tel 0733 312457

Pinner
Tel 01 868 1120

Reading
Tel 0734 587154

Redditch
Tel 0527 60266

Rotherham
Tel 0709 62523

Sheffield
Tel 0742 26575

Southend
Tel 0702 617716

Waltham Forest
Tel 01 521 7547

Welwyn Garden City/Hatfield
Tel 0707 327541

Wirral
Tel 051 652 1177

Parents Anonymous
London
Tel 01 263 8918

*Radio Piccadilly Family Care
 Line*
Manchester
Tel 061 236 9873

Rape Crisis Centres
Birmingham
Tel 021 233 2122

Brighton
Tel 0273 699756

Canterbury
Tel 0227 50400

Coventry
Tel 0203 57709

Dublin
Tel 601470

Edinburgh
Tel 031 556 9437

Leeds
Tel 0532 440058

Liverpool
Tel 051 709 1938

London
Tel 01 278 3956
    01 837 1600

Manchester
Tel 061 228 3602

Nottingham
Tel 0602 410440

Oxford
Tel 0865 726295

Portsmouth
Tel 0705 739366

Sheffield
Tel 0742 682480

Strathclyde
Tel 041 221 8448

Tyneside
Tel 0632 329858

Safeline
Bradford
Tell 0274 309909
Wed 9.00–13.00

SAVES
P O Box 40
Hull
Tel 0482 29990
Mon–Sat 18.00–22.00

TABOO
Manchester
Tel 061 236 1323

The Woman's Therapy Centre
6 Manor Gardens
London N7 6LA
Tel 01 263 6200
Send large SAE for list of
    groups and activities

Summary and recommendations

'Sexual abuse is defined as the involvement of dependent, developmentally immature children and adolescents in sexual activities they do not fully comprehend, or that violate the social taboos of family roles.' (Kempe and Kempe 1978: 60).

In this definition we include incest, as defined legally, sexual intercourse with children in other relationships, and other forms of sexual activity.

1 This definition should be adopted as a starting point for professionals.

RECOGNITION AND PROFESSIONAL RESPONSE (pp. 18–32)

Recognition of child sexual abuse is necessary as a stage in increasing the awareness of child abuse in the community. The number of cases that come to professional notice is far fewer than the number that actually occur. The reasons for this seem to be mainly connected with the complex and painful issues within the families in which the sexual abuse is taking place. In addition, children and other family members are often afraid to seek help because of their fear of punishment. Professionals may also fail to recognize child sexual abuse because of their own problems and difficulties.

2 Child sexual abuse should be regarded and dealt with as a form of child abuse.
3 For effective management of children and families, the different professionals who come into contact with child sexual abuse should work together.
4 Therapeutic and statutory measures should be combined to create a climate in which these children and their families, and others involved, can come forward for help.

Boys and girls can be involved in different abusive relationships and cases can present in direct and indirect ways.

5 Professionals in touch with children of all ages should be aware of the different patterns of presentation.
6 Professionals should also be aware of factors that put some families at special risk and preventive measures should be directed towards the families in which these high risk factors are known to be present.

The danger of rejection or further molestation of sexually abused children, or of increasing marital conflict, or the chance of family breakdown, is extremely high.

7 To diminish this danger, professionals should adopt a multidisciplinary approach that combines (legal) control with therapy for all the members of the family.

There are three stages in the recognition and management of child sexual abuse: suspicion and disclosure (the first twenty-four hours); initial case management, preliminary investigations and interviews (24 hours–3 days); and long-term management (3–21 days and longer).

8 The multidisciplinary approach should be adopted at each of these stages and the different professionals should know their roles and tasks at each stage.

STATUTORY AND THERAPEUTIC ISSUES (pp. 33–55)

9 The sexual abuse of children should be seen as a crime so that we can (a) define the limits of acceptable behaviour towards children, and (b) use it as a deterrent.

Prosecution

10 The protection and welfare of the children should be the primary concern of all those involved in dealing with these cases.

11 Investigation of suspected cases should take legal and medical factors into consideration.

12 The police should play a major part in investigation.

13 Decisions to arrest and charge should only be made by senior police officers.

14 The police should make contact with the social services departments or the National Society for the Prevention of Cruelty to Children (NSPCC) before such decisions are made, except in cases of emergency.

15 Child abuse liaison officers (police) should be appointed in all areas in the UK to work with the child abuse co-ordinators appointed by social services departments (described on pp. 36–8). This practice has been developed by the Devon and Cornwall Constabulary (*Devon Multidisciplinary Child Abuse Handbook* 1984).

The protection of the child can often be ensured without prosecution of the alleged perpetrator. However, we recognize that the graver the case the more likely it is that prosecution will be necessary to protect the child and in the public interest.

16 Cautioning should be used more often and, rather than instituting prosecution procedures, appropriate cases should be left on file.

The present judicial system: criminal proceedings
(pp. 34–49)

17(a) Affidavit evidence or video recordings taken by the professional dealing with the case should be admissable; and (b) judges should be encouraged to intervene to ensure that children are protected from insensitive handling by lawyers in court.

Recommendations 17 (a) and (b) will reduce the trauma to children in court, but the right of the defendant to test a child's evidence should remain.

18(a) An especially expedited hearing process should be created, and the maximum period of delay between charge and trial should be no more than three months (this procedure already exists in Scotland for all criminal cases); and (b) a special procedure to hold the hearing even earlier should be available on application by any defendant who admits the allegation and intends pleading guilty.

19 Therapeutic work should begin at the earliest opportunity, preferably by means of a family meeting. At this meeting all family members should be present and the fact of, and responsibility for, the abuse should be acknowledged. The police and legal advisers should be notified of the meeting so that if it precedes a trial this is not prejudiced nor is the evidence polluted.

Prison sentences are destructive to the family and can be more damaging than the effects of the abuse itself. Although multiple offences and abuse of young children are likely to attract a prison sentence, a probation order with a requirement of treatment is often satisfactory.

20 The probation order (the maximum length of which is three years) with a requirement of treatment and separate residence for the perpetrator should be the preferred way of dealing with these cases. We do not recommend the deferred sentence because its maximum duration is only six months and it has no provision for treatment.

The present judicial system: civil proceedings (pp. 49–50)

21 Civil proceedings to safeguard and promote the welfare of the child victim should not be delayed but should proceed at the same time as, or before, criminal proceedings.

Confidentiality (pp. 52–5)

22 The guidelines on confidentiality for professionals issued

in relationship to physical abuse should be extended to sexual abuse. Protection of the children, if necessary, should take precedence over confidentiality between a therapist and an adult patient who discloses sexual abuse.

MANAGEMENT (pp. 56–106)

23 An experienced, multidisciplinary group should be available in each geographical area in the UK to provide advice and support for professionals.

24 When there is a risk of, or actual additional, physical violence, sexual abuse should be dealt with in the same way as physical abuse but no unplanned precipitate actions should be taken, and professionals working together should establish that the child is not a continuing risk of abuse.

25 No one professional should take sole responsibility for the management of a case of child sexual abuse and ways should be found to convince the professionals involved – police, social workers, doctors, probation officers, lawyers and judges – of the value of this approach.

26 The stage-by-stage system of intervention described above (pp. 81–4) and developed by the NSPCC Special Unit and Family Centre, Northamptonshire, should be adopted throughout the UK.

27 Guidelines for talking with children about sexual matters should be available for all professionals who may come into contact with possible cases of sexual abuse. These guidelines should include advice for the initial interview and investigation as well as for the later stages of management. Professionals carrying out interviews and investigation should be especially trained for this work.

28 The methods for long-term management of these families described above (pp. 85–91) and developed in such therapeutic programmes as the Sexual Abuse Treatment Project at the Hospital for Sick Children, Great Ormond Street, London (Furniss, Bingley-Miller, and Bentovim 1984), should be adopted throughout the UK.

PREVENTION (pp. 107–16)

Prevention is best achieved by group discussions at school.

29 Specific school programmes to teach personal safety skills to children should be devised. The issue of appropriate and inappropriate touch should be made especially clear. Teachers and parents as well as children should be involved in these programmes. It should be recognized that the adults who need training first are the professionals themselves.

30 All children at risk should have an opportunity for confidential discussion, suited to their age and stage of development, with an individual they can trust.

31 Guidelines for prevention and education should be available for each professional group that may come into contact with possible cases of child sexual abuse.

The present fears associated with revealing sexual abuse mean that victims and offenders understandably wish for anonymity.

32 Crisis telephone lines and self-help and voluntary groups should be established and professionals should maintain close contact with them.

33 In-service and multidisciplinary training schemes should be established. These schemes should be planned not only to convey information about management but also to respond to the personal issues evoked by the sexual abuse of children.

34 The protection and welfare of the children should be the primary concern of all those involved in the investigation, management, and prevention of child sexual abuse.

Appendix – case reports

ELEANOR, CHARLIE, AND ALAN: BROTHER/SISTER INCEST

This case report describes incest between a girl and her two brothers in a chaotic and disorganized family. The mother was referred to the police by the social services following a co-ordinating meeting. The professionals present at this meeting were a medical practitioner (chairman), a police officer, an education officer, an education welfare officer, a head teacher, a nursing officer and a health visitor (from the area health authority), the divisional director of social services, two senior social workers, two social workers, and the co-ordinator, also a social worker. Successful co-operation between the police, the social services, a voluntary group and other agencies involved has resulted in a satisfactory outcome.

Family structure

Father, aged 39.
Mother, aged 37.
Charlie, aged 15.
Eleanor, aged 14.
Alan, aged 11.

All the individuals involved in the sexual abuse were juveniles. The family was known to the social services department, two of the children being listed in the 'at risk' category in the social services child abuse register. The third child was listed in the same register as 'suspected'.

There was a long and complex history of domestic difficulties in the family as a whole. The mother had a history of psychiatric illness, the father had been convicted of minor crimes, and the two boys had come to the notice of police on previous occasions. The education authorities had reported particular problems with the children. Eleanor and the older brother, Charlie, attended a special secondary school for difficult and educationally subnormal children; the younger brother, Alan, had not attended school for some months before the offence.

The matter came to light when the mother took Eleanor to the family practitioner and alleged that both her husband and her elder son had been having intercourse with Eleanor. The general practitioner prescribed the contraceptive pill. The mother then went to the social services department and repeated the allegations. By this time she and Eleanor were in a home for battered wives.

The police in this area had been continually involved with the social services and other agencies in case conferences and review meetings for a number of years and were aware of the categories in which the children had been placed on the child abuse register. When interviewed by the police, Eleanor denied that her father had ever interfered with her sexually and no evidence was forthcoming to support the mother's allegation. Eleanor alleged, however, and there was evidence to support the fact, that Charlie and Alan had indulged in sexual practices including intercourse with her for at least two-and-a-half years. Charlie was interviewed in the presence of a member of a victim support unit (representing his father) and admitted to all the alleged acts. Alan was interviewed in the presence of his father and also admitted all that was alleged. Because of his age, the only offence that he could be charged with in law was indecent assault.

Following the report to the police, the social services department and other agencies were kept fully informed and a number of meetings were held with members of these agencies and police officers. It was felt by all concerned that no prosecution should be recommended, but Eleanor was taken into the care of the local authority on a voluntary basis for a period of six months. Unfortunately, her mother removed her and took her back to the family home where her brothers were living. After consultation with the agencies concerned, the police removed her the next day to a place of safety. She appeared at a juvenile court and a twenty-eight-day interim care order was granted on the application of the police. A full care order was granted one month later on application by the social services. Both the boys were cautioned.

During the next two years the key worker, who was a social worker, worked with the family. Charlie left school; he continued to live at home and had two jobs during this time. Alan committed minor offences, was ruled to be beyond parental control, and was taken into care.

At the age of sixteen, Eleanor was still in care and the local authorities arranged for her to take an oral contraceptive again. She was in regular contact with her mother who from time to time left home and returned to a battered wives' hostel, but her father was only permitted to see her at the place where she resided in care. There was another younger boy who had also been removed into care due to the continual upheavals in the family.

Two years later, at the age of eighteen, Eleanor has left school, where she did well, and is training at an adult training centre. The family have reunited and the father is living at home again.

SARAH AND PAMELA AND THEIR FAMILY: MULTIPLE SEXUAL ABUSE

This case report describes a family in which multiple sexual offences were occurring. The father had had sexual intercourse with his daughter, aged fourteen, and had also committed buggery with his thirteen-year-old son who, in turn, had had sexual intercourse with his sister, as had another brother. The standards of intelligence and nutrition of all the family members were low. In spite of good co-operation between police and other agencies, the outlook for the children in this family is poor.

The abuse came to light when the father was arrested for assaulting his daughter, Pamela. Whilst he was in custody the mother informed the police of her suspicion that he had been having intercourse with another daughter, Sarah.

Family stucture

Father: aged 45, a builder's labourer.
Paul: aged 19.
Sarah: aged 14.
Phillip: aged 13.
Pamela: aged 11.

The mother said that she had been too frightened to do anything until the father was in custody. Statements were recorded from the mother and daughter and a medical examination by the police surgeon verified that some person had had intercourse with Sarah. The father was interviewed by police and admitted that he had been committing indecent acts with Sarah from a very early age, by handling the girl's private parts and by inciting her to masturbate him. He further admitted the offence of incest and also that, many years before, he had indecently assaulted a daughter by a previous marriage. He was extremely co-operative and readily admitted that he had indecently assaulted Phillip and committed buggery with him. This was later agreed by Phillip. When interviewed, both Phillip and his brother Paul admitted committing offences against Sarah. To give some idea of the degree to which the girl had become perverted, she volunteered the fact (and evidence was obtained) that she had incited a dog to have intercourse with her and that she carried out other indecent acts herself. The father remained in custody and the brothers were living away from home.

Within forty-eight hours of the matter coming to police attention, a case conference was arranged. The professionals present at this meeting were the social services co-ordinator (chairman), a police officer, a nursing officer, a health visitor, a school nurse (area health authority), a probation officer, a school teacher, a senior social worker, two social workers, and a social work administrator.

After this meeting, Sarah was placed on the child abuse register in the category of 'confirmed (sexual abuse)'; the younger sister Pamela was placed on the register in the 'at risk' category. The key worker was a social worker and the matter was to be reviewed within two months. A probation officer continued to work with Phillip who was already receiving his attention. Both girls were of low intelligence and their school records were not good.

Subsequently, the father was sentenced to four years' imprisonment. The only action taken against the brothers was to caution them. Within twelve months it was necessary to take out full care orders in respect of both girls due to their general behaviour and the fact that they committed criminal offences. And so the situation remains. The father has now been placed on parole and, therefore, the two daughters are not allowed visits to the home. Sarah is in a foster home and Pamela is in a community home. Parental contact is being fully supervised.

ANGELA: SEXUAL ABUSE AND REJECTION

In this case report we describe what happened to a fourteen-year old girl who was first sexually abused by her father and subsequently rejected by both parents. The girl told a school teacher about a sexual relationship with her father. The head teacher called the father to the school and informed the police.

Father was interviewed by the head teacher and vehemently denied the accusations. Police officers then joined the interview and were informed by the father that he had recently chastized his daughter because she was staying out at night and running around with undesirable boys. At this point the girl was interviewed by the police in the presence of her father. She acknowledged that she slept with boys and told lies. Finally, when invited to do so, she retracted her accusations against her father.

That evening the girl was met from school by a grim-faced step-mother. None of the family spoke to her for the rest of the week and on Saturday morning her step-mother packed the girl's bags and her father drove her to another part of town. Her bags were dumped on a doorstep, she was given five pounds, and informed that there was a bed-sitting room reserved for her in the house. At the age of fourteen she was abandoned by her family;

she never saw them again. She continued to attend school but the teachers never learned of her change of address and there was no follow-up by the police or social services.

The girl, who in fact had never had intercourse with anyone but her father, felt degraded, dirty, and wicked. She became extremely socially isolated apart from a job she obtained in a newsagents. By working at evenings and weekends she supported herself entirely. At about the age of sixteen she embarked on a frenetic period of sexual promiscuity and heavy drinking but at the age of eighteen eventually pulled herself together and began a period of study which enabled her to obtain a professional qualification. She still suffers periodic bouts of depression and has a poor opinion of herself.

JOHN: THE BREAK-UP OF A FAMILY

John, a man in his thirties, had experienced a disastrous marriage in his teens when his wife ridiculed his lack of potency and left him after a year during which she had many extramarital affairs. John became a solitary person with few interests outside his work. A few years later he offered his help to a new neighbour, Janet, a nurse in training, who was pregnant but unmarried. She had been abandoned by the man with whom she had been living and was now in poor accommodation which she was trying to renovate.

Family structure

John, aged 36, step-father to the eldest daughter and father of the two younger daughters.
Janet, aged 29.
Three daughters, aged 12, 10, and 9 at the time sexual abuse was disclosed.

After the birth of her child, of whom John became very fond, John and Janet drifted into an intimate relationship. She was able to overcome his sexual inhibitions and reassure him of his masculinity. They eventually married and had two daughters. John's business flourished and all went well until Janet decided to resume her nursing training. She worked long hours and on qualifying obtained a job on a late shift with the result that the couple saw little of each other. As John came home Janet went out and when she returned late at night she was tired and eager to get to sleep.

The girls were now aged twelve, ten and nine. They and their father were very fond of each other and spent the evenings playing together and usually, in the finish, all sitting on the settee, the girls in their nightdresses, watching television. Sexual contact between the parents had virtually ceased. One evening as the eldest girl lay across her father's knee he began to caress her breasts. This occurred on several successive evenings, the explorations advanced, and the father had an erection that excited some curiosity in the children and he eventually exposed himself. A regular pattern of fondling developed into playful masturbation and then the eldest girl was 'sat' on her father's knee until penetration occurred. Although sworn to secrecy she told her mother of this play and Janet went straight to the police. The three girls were taken to the police station, statements were obtained, and the girls were examined by a police surgeon. All three were distressed and bewildered. On the basis of these statements the husband was arrested at work and taken into custody. He admitted the offences and pleaded guilty but remained in custody.

During the next three months the mother became depressed and neglected the children. She was angry with her eldest child and blamed her both for not telling her earlier and for 'encouraging' her father. The girl became a problem at school and at her mother's request was taken into care.

After three months the father was sentenced to three years' imprisonment. His wife was now riddled with guilt because she felt she had forced him into the acts by her work and sexual disinterest. She was angry and resentful of her eldest daughter and neglectful of the younger girls. The house in which they lived was part of her husband's business which was declared bankrupt; they were, therefore, housed in a council flat in a poor area.

At no time was any help offered to the children. Janet was 'treated' for depression but the psychiatrist had no contact with the children or their social worker. Social work help focused entirely on practical issues of money, housing, and care.

The poor outcomes in the cases of Angela and John are due in large part to the precipitate and poorly thought-out action of the police and other professionals involved and to the lack of any effective follow-up.

DANIELLE AND HER FAMILY: A CASE HISTORY OF FAMILY THERAPY

This report describes the therapy of a family in which sexual abuse had been occurring. The initial investigations, with the first family meetings, the work with individual family members in separate groups, the middle therapeutic steps, and the long-term management are described. Two family meetings that included the father, one of which was held in the prison in which he was in custody and one after his release, are described. Verbatim reports from family meetings are included.

Danielle, aged thirteen, was referred by a social worker to a department of child psychiatry in a children's hospital following a recent disclosure that her father had been abusing her sexually.

Initial investigations

In response to the referral from the social worker, the psychiatrist and the psychiatric social worker assigned to the case invited the mother and her two daughters, with their community social worker, to a meeting where the following information was obtained.

Family structure

> Father: Ian, aged 36, a manual worker in an engineering maintenance firm.
> Mother: Maureen, aged 34, a housewife.
> Danielle, aged 13, attended a local comprehensive school.
> Samantha, aged 11, attended a local school for educationally sub-normal (mild) children. She was also epileptic and had a mild right hemiparesis.

Development of the sexual abuse and initial response

Although it was learned later that sexual abuse had been going on for some years, the initial information was that there had been a few recent occurrences only, the last one culminating in attempted intercourse. The sexual abuse had occurred whilst the father was under the influence of alcohol and the mother was out playing bingo. However, on the most recent occasion, late one evening, the mother was looking after the younger sister who was having an epileptic fit. She was alerted by Danielle's cries and caught the father in the act. She gathered the girls together and departed with them to the local police station. Danielle was immediately medically examined by a police surgeon and interviewed at length. She revealed that her father's threats that he would put her into care and take away her stereo recorder had prevented her from telling anyone about the abuse until now. The father was taken into custody and was remanded until his trial when he pleaded guilty and received a four-year sentence. There was a charge of indecent assault and buggery of his wife as well as the sexual abuse of his daughter.

The police informed the social services department and a social worker was assigned to work with the family. At first the mother expressed her intention to divorce her husband; there was great concern about his return to the family.

Family of origin

The father, Ian, came from a large disorganized working-class family in Scotland; the mother, Maureen, was illegitimate and was initially cared for by her maternal grandparents. The subsequent family relationships were complex. Maureen's mother married another man (i.e. not Maureen's father) and had three children. Maureen joined this family but was almost certainly sexually abused by her step-father and, because of the difficulties with him and also with her own mother, she was the subject of a care order when she was eleven years old and remained in care until she was sixteen.

Present family

The parents met whilst Ian was working in the south, and from the beginning the marriage was stormy and bedevilled by financial difficulties. The first major crisis was Samantha's illness: when she was six weeks old she had an attack of meningitis that left her with a right hemiparesis and subject to frequent epileptic fits. Over the next few years Maureen's preoccupation with

Samantha's health led to relative neglect of her older daughter with the result that, at the age of six years, Danielle was soiling herself and showing other behavioural difficulties. The social services were intermittently involved and Danielle was referred to a child guidance clinic at that time.

Maureen had several miscarriages and two stillbirths – both boys. She was found to have an early carcinoma of the uterus and had a hysterectomy. This operation finally deprived Ian of all hope of having the son he longed for. At this time Danielle was seven years old.

Ian turned to drinking – at home – and Maureen took on the task of supplying beer for him. She increasingly shielded him from the realities of family hardship and she looked after the family budget. Ian worked throughout this period but always for low pay. He had one brief spell of in-patient treatment for his drinking problem, but his drinking continued.

Reports of family life and relationships described the marital relationship as distant and unconfiding. Maureen was very close to Samantha and she was also working as a child-minder, looking after other people's babies. Danielle was close to her father. There was little contact with Ian's family and although there had been support from Maureen's maternal grandparents this had stopped when the grandfather died. The relationship with Maureen's parents was difficult and her step-father in particular was hostile to Maureen and her present family.

Observations confirmed the distance between Maureen and Danielle and the closeness between Maureen and Samantha. The family's tendency to create dramas, e.g. Maureen's way of describing events, and Samantha's authentic fits, and 'pseudo' fits also. Maureen's anger with her husband contrasted with Danielle's sense of guilt that her father was in prison. Maureen also admitted to feeling angry with Danielle at times.

Initial therapeutic steps

Arrangements were made for Danielle to join a girls' group, for Maureen to join a mothers' group, and for regular family meetings that included the local social workers. The first concern about cessation of the sexual abuse had been dealt with by the father's imprisonment at the time of referral; and the fact that he had accepted responsibility by pleading guilty had removed the immediate threat that the parents would come together and reject Danielle. The social services' personnel, before Danielle's referral to the child psychiatry department, had decided to initiate care proceedings (this was before the sentence was known). The mother's earlier wish for divorce did not persist and the social workers were concerned that the sympathy shown by her to her husband and her expressed wish not to lose him might put the children at risk. Both children's names were put on the non-accidental injury record kept by the local authority. Both children expressed love for their father and said that they missed him.

Initial family sessions took place without the father but once Maureen and Danielle were established in their respective groups negotiations began with the prison medical staff to arrange for a family meeting in prison. In this way there could be an open sharing of responsibility and the beginning of treatment for the whole family.

Maureen attended the mothers' group and increasingly re-cognized her own part in what had happened. She was re-considering the idea of divorce. She realized, for example, that she had been responsible for supplying her husband with drink, and for patronizing him by concealing problems from him. Her closeness to Samantha, too, had led to her excluding Ian and allowing his increasing closeness to Danielle. It was as if she had become a compulsively caring parent and Ian had acted as if he was her child alongside Danielle, whereas to Danielle he was the parent, 'in control' of his daughter and demanding a sexual relationship with her.

The early phases of the work in Danielle's group focused on her talking about what had happened to her and comparing her experiences with those of other teenage girls in the group. She became a helpful and responsible group member. She was able to express her sadness at the loss of the father, her nightmarish memories of her experiences, and her concern about the future, particularly when she thought about his drinking and the effect this had on him. She worried about the change that would be needed before it would be safe for him to return home. She also spoke a great deal about the victimization that she and her family had been subjected to by neighbours and at school; this had led to a change of school and the family had been forced to move house. The work in her group helped to bring Danielle and her mother together and there were fewer complaints that Maureen spoiled Samantha and was unfair to Danielle.

An early family session focused on the need to spell out matters for Samantha and, specifically, to bring her knowledge of the sexual abuse into the open. She was present at the first meeting, when sexual abuse had been admitted, but as with many children she managed to 'forget' what she thought others did not want her to know.

The following is an extract from the family session.

Therapist: I'm not sure if Samantha knows why her father is in prison.

Mother: She knows he's done something wrong but she doesn't know exactly what, she knows it was serious.

Therapist [directing the question at Danielle]: What do you imagine Samantha thinks something serious is?

Danielle: Because he did something to you [meaning herself].

Therapist: Is that right Samantha?

Samantha: He did something to Danielle, something rude.

Therapist [checking with mother]: Did you know this?

Mother: I knew she thought something had happened to Danielle, something that should not have happened. Exactly how much she knew we don't know. We're too frightened of saying too much in front of Samantha because of her fits. She dotes on her dad so we try to keep as quiet as possible in front of her. [This was an attempt to establish a link between Danielle and herself as the two parents who cared for Samantha.]

Therapist [reassuring mother]: We might as well find out what she knows. Samantha, what would something rude be exactly?

Samantha: Doing something really rude, putting something into her.

Therapist: What would be put into her that would be rude? [Therapist pauses and then decides to explore through knowledge about birth.] Do you know how babies are made and come out?

Samantha: Some are born in test-tubes(!) and some are born ordinarily.

Therapist: How are they born ordinarily?

Samantha: The doctor does an operation?

Therapist: I remember the last time we discussed this you couldn't remember the usual way! Can you remember today?

How did Danielle and you come out of mummy? [Silence] [To Danielle]: Can you remind her how babies are born? [This question is also to help Danielle to speak about a painful subject and to ensure that talking about sexual matters becomes open in the family.]

Danielle: You come out of mother's vagina.

Therapist: Does Samantha know there are two openings at the bottom, one at the back for your motions and one at the front where your wees come out and the babies do too?

Samantha: Yes.

Mother: She's seen about it on television but she's never taken much interest in it [confirming that parents think children know less than they do] . . . I don't cover such things up.

Therapist: Yes I remember you told us that you and your husband had told the children the facts of life before matters came out. So how do the babies get in?

Danielle: The daddy and the mummy go to bed together. The daddy puts his penis in the mummy's vagina and puts in the sperm and it touches the egg which can accept it or reject it and can get bigger – then the baby grows.

Therapist [to Samantha]: So how old do you have to be to have a baby? Could you have a baby?

Samantha: No.

Therapist: Could Danielle have a baby? She might be able to. [To Danielle] Have you started your periods yet?

Danielle: I've had one.

Therapist: You know about periods. Can you explain that to Samantha?

Danielle: I've forgotten. It's something to do with the egg, and passing it every month if it's not been fertilized.

Therapist [to Samantha]: If making a baby is putting the daddy's penis into the mummy's vagina, how old do you have to be for that to happen – to have intercourse – could it be when you're little or grown up?

Samantha: When you're grown up.

Therapist: If it happens when you're little and not grown up, that's . . . rude . . . as you wouldn't be grown up enough to have that happen. I have a feeling you know what happened between your daddy and Danielle. That she wasn't old enough for it to happen, and it was also wrong as she was his daughter, and that meant the police came and your daddy had to go to

court and then to prison. You knew that didn't you?
Samantha: Yes.
Therapist: But you didn't know it was all right for you to know.

The early phases of treatment, with the father away, lasted some four or five months until arrangements could be made for a family meeting at which he could be present.

Middle therapeutic steps

The next period of therapeutic work was focused on the family meeting in prison with the father. He had already met Maureen and the children during visits on prison visiting days so contact had been established.

In her group Danielle continued at times to complain that her mother was 'picking on her', criticizing her behaviour, and favouring Samantha. She was trying to get closer to the male therapist in the group and to reject the female therapist. She was saying openly that she wished her father was at home and that 'he was at least fair'.

At a family meeting much new information was disclosed. Danielle told her mother she wanted to be 'in care' so that she could help her father and ensure that he could come home earlier. She also said that she thought her mother knew even before matters had come into the open that there had been something sexual going on, and that although she had told the police that she had tried to stop her husband in fact she had not.

'My dad asked my mum if he could "show me what life was about" and my mum had said "yes". That's when I went downstairs and got a knife. But my dad chucked it out of my hand. That's when it happened, and it happened again in their bedroom. He said he wanted to speak to me and it happened again. If I tell the police that my mum will get into trouble.'

The family meeting in prison

The prison meeting included all members of the family, the social worker, the prison probation officer (who had had some individual sessions with father), the community probation officer (who had prepared a report), the father's therapist from a prison group (he attended a group meeting daily), and the therapist from the department of child psychiatry. The meeting was difficult because the objectives were to help the family to speak about what had happened and to continue to discuss it openly. However, the full extent of the sexual abuse was revealed by Danielle reminding her father of many episodes that he had forgotten because he had been drunk. The seriousness of his drinking came to light as did his unrealistically optimistic views about his ability to stay sober and to work. On a more realistic level, however, from the first meeting in prison the parents took full responsibility for the sexual abuse. They both showed an optimistic view about the future and were keen to get together again.

The following is an extract from the parents' discussion about responsibility. This exchange took place at another family meeting, but the same professionals and family members were present.

Therapist: Do you think in the long run, although it's very distressing to be in prison, that you will be grateful to your wife?

Father: It's been a blessing in disguise. The fact of going to prison has brought the family closer.

Mother: We're more open.

Father: I wouldn't have been here today. I would have left the family. That's what was on my mind. She wouldn't listen if I mentioned Danielle. I was always being accused of taking her side. That's stopped now. We can sit and listen to each other. I sit in my group and I take one hundred per cent responsibility, and my wife in hers. It's both our faults. Neither of us was prepared to listen.

Mother: We never sat down and talked things over.

Therapist [to Danielle]: Did you hear that? Both your parents are taking responsibility.

Mother: If there was a bill came in, sooner than go up to him and say there was a hundred pound bill in, I kept it from him. I knew he'd go for the drink and then all hell would be let loose. I tried to pay it myself and it was wrong.

Father: Danielle would come to me with problems she should have gone to her mother with.

Danielle: I've always been closer to my dad.

Mother: That was my fault, my time was wrapped up with Samantha, so many hospitals, Danielle was with her father. I was in hospital and both were with their father. It was one disaster as far as Danielle was concerned. She was scared of me.

At a later stage of therapy both parents could take the important step of accepting responsibility, thus helping to free Danielle from feeling guilty and rejected. Following the family session in prison Danielle became far more assertive, both at school and at home, and she was less dramatic in asking for special attention in her group; she could now give support to the other girls. But she remained extremely anxious at times about her father's returning home and the possibility of the sexual abuse starting again.

The task of the girls' group was very much concerned with the issues of who to tell and how to tell; with establishing a network of people to confide in; and with defining when touching is appropriate and when it is abusive.

Long-term management: preparation for the future and discharge from prison

A further family meeting took place about five months after the previous one, at a time when Ian had served one year of his sentence and was due to be considered for discharge from prison on parole. After much resistance he was now finding the group in prison helpful and was himself being more co-operative and open. He now regarded the agencies involved – the social and probation services – as helping the family to reunite rather than trying to split them up (as he had felt previously). Both parents were strikingly united on the theme of Ian's return home and were surprised that the professionals expected him to live in a hostel. Maureen, however, said that she would choose her children rather than her husband if there was any recurrence of the abuse, and they agreed to a period of separation.

Many concerns were expressed for the future. It was thought important that the father should join a group at the hospital. It was suggested that Maureen and Danielle continue in their groups. Although this was longer than they needed as far as their ability to talk with each other was concerned, it was felt that Danielle, although she continued to talk with her social worker, also needed her group.

The probation officer was concerned about the father's drinking. It was no test not to drink in a secure setting. He had always drunk at home and would probably start to do so again. The probation officer also thought that there was a degree of lip-service about Ian's acceptance of his responsibility and that there was some falseness in this attitude. It was also generally realized that the difficulties between the parents, particularly the break-down of the parents' sexual relationship, had not been dealt with. The parents' early desire to get back together and their apparent understanding of what had caused the problems, particularly the distance between Danielle and her mother, could be another example of the conflict avoidance (see p. 12) so characteristic of this family.

This case report illustrates the difficulties of dealing with family problems thoroughly when one parent is in prison. He cannot join the family meetings, when this is precisely what is needed to deal with the painful issues of separation and rejection connected with sexual abuse and the events that follow its disclosure. In spite of these difficulties, Danielle and her mother made progress. They were more in touch with each other and with their real problems. Ian, because he was separated from the family, made less progress and at times even held back or reversed therapeutic advances in other members of the family.

As part of the parole arrangements Ian was prohibited from staying at home. Because there was such good rapport between the family and the therapists, combined with a willingness to work, it was possible to agree about his living in a hostel. There was also agreement about continued group and family meetings with the child psychiatric team and with the social worker and probation officer who were seeing the family at home. A care order was not needed, and proceedings for this had been dropped after sentence. This also meant, of course, that continuing contact with the social workers could only be on a voluntary basis.

The therapists' view was that only direct continuing contact between members of the family could bring all these issues into the open. The prospects for family meetings were good because (a) through work in her group Danielle had become more able to assert herself; (b) Maureen, similarly, had become more committed to protecting Danielle; and (c) the professionals felt that their network could deal with the risks involved. Everyone felt pleasure, as well as concern, at the prospect of the family coming together.

Conclusions

This case illustrates the many issues involved and the therapeutic work that is necessary to help a family where rejection and sexual abuse have been taking place for a long time. The mother's family background contributed to her marrying a man whose self-esteem was low and who needed her care and protection as a child might. This led to tension and difficulties between husband and wife. The illness and handicap of the younger child triggered Maureen's compulsive caretaking, and the miscarriages, the stillbirths, and the hysterectomy, continued the process, increasing the distance and lack of understanding between the couple. Ian reacted by drinking, which stimulated his sexual impulses towards the older daughter, already neglected by her mother, as a way of building-up his confidence in himself.

Nevertheless, they are an appealing family. The professionals all felt they wanted to help them, perhaps taking the place of the helping, supporting grandparents. The need to protect Danielle, who is scapegoat and sexual partner, constantly had to be kept in mind while helping the parents to come to terms with their own relationship, now viewed more realistically and on a more equal basis. Ian and Maureen, as adults, had been trying to make up for their experiences as children with the result that patterns of rejection from their past were being repeated in the present. Therapy enabled these two parents to look after the children's needs and the needs of the family as a whole without the continuous intrusion of their own problems.

References

Anderson, D. (1979) Touching; When is it Caring and Nurturing or When is it Exploitative and Damaging? *Child Abuse and Neglect* 3: 793–94.

Baker, T. (1983) Sexual Abuse within the Family. *19* April: 35–40.

BASPCAN (British Association for the Study and Prevention of Child Abuse and Neglect) (1981) *Child Sexual Abuse*. London: BASPCAN.

Bentovim, A. and Bingley-Miller, L. (in preparation) Parenting and Parenting Failure – Some Guidelines for the Assessment of the Child, His Parents and His Family.

Brassard, M.R., Tyler, A.H., and Kehle, T.J. (1983) School Programs to Prevent Intrafamilial Child Sexual Abuse. *Child Abuse and Neglect* 7: 214–45.

Burton, L. (1968) *Vulnerable Children*. London: Routledge & Kegan Paul.

Children and Young Persons Act (1933) Section 37.

Children and Young Persons Act (1969) Section 47.

Cmnd 8092 (1981) Royal Commission on Criminal Procedure. London: HMSO.

Cmnd 9048 (1979–82) Home Office Statistics on Criminal Offences in

England and Wales. London: HMSO.

Cmnd 9213 (1984) Criminal Law Revision Committee, Report no. 15. London: HMSO.

Cook, M. and Howells, H.K. (eds) (1981) *Adult Sexual Interest in Children*. London: Academic Press.

Cooper, I. (1978) De-criminalization of Incest – New Legal/ Clinical Responses. In J.M. Eekelaar and S.W. Katz (eds) *Family Violence*. London: Butterworth.

Criminal Law Revision Committee (1980) Working Party on Sexual Offences. London: HMSO.

Devon Multi-disciplinary Child Abuse Handbook (1984) 2nd edn. Investigation – Agency Procedures. Exeter: Devon Constabulary.

DHSS/Home Office (1976) Non-accidental Injury to Children: The Police and Case Conferences. LASSL (76) 2 CMO (76) 2 p(iv), 25.

DHSS/Welsh Office (1978) Release of Prisoners Convicted of Offences Against Children in the Home. LAC (78) 22 Welsh Office Circular 107/78.

DHSS (1980) Child Abuse: Central Register Systems Circular LASSL (80) 4 HN (80) 20.

DHSS (1982) Child Abuse. A Study of Inquiry Reports 1973–1981. London: HMSO.

Finkelhor, D. (1979) Sexually Victimized Children. New York: The Free Press.

Finkelhor, D. (1980) Risk Factors in the Sexual Victimization of Children . *Child Abuse and Neglect* 4: 265–73.

Finkelhor, D. (1981) Long-term Effects of Childhood Sexual Victimization in a Non-Clinical Sample. Proceeding of the second International Conference on Child Abuse, Amsterdam.

Finkelhor, D. (1982) Sexual Abuse – a Sociological Perspective. *Child Abuse and Neglect* 6: 95–102.

Freud, A. (1981) A Psychoanalyst's View of Sexual Abuse by Parents. In P.B. Mrazek and C.H. Kempe, (eds) *Sexually Abused Children and their Families*. Oxford: Pergamon Press.

Fritz, G.S., Stoll, K., and Wagner, N.N. (1981) A Comparison of Males and Females Who Were Sexually Molested as Children. *Journal of Sex and Marital Therapy* 7: 54–9.

Furniss, T. (1983) Mutual Influence and Interlocking Professional-family Process in the Treatment of Child Sexual Abuse and Incest. *Child Abuse and Neglect* 7: 207–23.

Furniss, T. (1985) Conflict-avoiding and Conflict-regulating Patterns in Incest and Child Sexual Abuse. *Acta Paedopsychiatrica* 50: 6.

Furniss, T., Bingley-Miller, L., and Bentovim, A. (1984) Therapeutic Approach to Sexual Abuse. *Archives of Disease in Childhood* 59 (9): 865–70.

General Medical Council (1983) *Professional Conduct and Discipline: Fitness to Practise.* London: General Medical Council.

Giarretto, H. (1976) Humanistic Treatment of Father-daughter Incest. In R.E. Helfer and C.H. Kempe (eds) *Child Abuse and Neglect – the Family and the Community.* Cambridge, Mass.: Ballinger.

Giarretto, H. (1977) Humanistic Treatment of Father-daughter Incest. *Child Abuse and Neglect* 1: 411–26.

Giarretto, H. (1981a) Without Prejudice. *Social Work Today* 13/14: 8–10.

Giarretto, H. (1981b) A Comprehensive Child Sexual Abuse Treatment Program. In P.B. Mrazek and C.H. Kempe (eds) *Sexually Abused Children and their Families.* Oxford: Pergamon Press.

Goodwin, J. (1981) Suicide Attempts in Sexual Abuse Victims and their Mothers. *Child Abuse and Neglect* 5: 217–21.

Herman, J.L. (1981) Father-daughter Incest. Cambridge, Mass.: Harvard University Press.

Johnson, C.L. (1981) Case Handling through Public Social Agencies in South-east USA. *Child Abuse and Neglect* 5: 123–28.

Kempe, R.S. and Kempe, C.H. (1978) *Child Abuse.* London: Fontana/Open Books.

Lukianowicz, N. (1972) Incest: I Paternal Incest; II Other Types of Incest. *British Journal of Psychiatry* 120: 301–03.

Magistrates' Court Act (1980) Section 6.

McGuire, R.J., Carlisle, J.M., and Young, B.G. (1965) Sexual Deviation as Conditioned Behaviour: a Hypothesis. *Behaviour Research and Therapy* 3: 185–90.

Meiselman, K. (1978) *Incest: A Psychological Study of Causes and Effects with Treatment Recommendations.* San Francisco, Calif.: Jossey Bass.

Mental Health Act (1983) Section 12(2).

Metropolitan Chairmen's Special Committee on Child Abuse (1980) *An Introduction to the Preventive Education Project for Children.* Toronto, Canada.

Mrazek, P.B., Lynch, M., and Bentovim. A. (1981) Recognition of Child Sexual Abuse in the United Kingdom. In P.B. Mrazek and C.H. Kempe (eds) *Sexually Abused Children and their Families.* Oxford: Pergamon Press.

——(1983) Sexual Abuse of Children in the United Kingdom. *Child Abuse and Neglect* 7: 147–54.

Okell Jones, C. and Bentovim, A. (1984) Sexual Abuse of Children: Fleeting Trauma or Lasting Disaster. In E.J. Anthony (ed.) *Year Book of the International Association of Child Psychiatry.* New York: Wiley.

Ounsted, C. (1975) Gaze Aversion in Child Abuse. *World Medicine* 10 (17): 27.

Pascoe, D.J. (1979) Management of Sexually Abused Children. *Pediatric*

Annals **8**(5): 309–16.

Pincus, L. and Dare, C. (1978) *Secrets in the Family*. London: Faber & Faber.

Powers of Criminal Courts Act (1973)

Rosenfeld, A.A. and Newberger, E.H. (1977) Compassion Versus Control: Conceptual and Practical Pitfalls in the Broadened Definition of Child Abuse. *Journal of the American Medical Association* **237**: 2086–088.

Royal College of Psychiatrists (1982) Emotional Abuse of Children – A Discussion Paper. *Bulletin of the Royal College of Psychiatry* **6**: 85–7.

Russell, D.E.H. (1983) The Incidence and Prevalence of Intrafamilial and Extrafamilial Sexual Abuse of Female Children. *Child Abuse and Neglect* **7**: 147–54.

Sgroi, S.M. (1975) Sexual Molestation of Children: the Last Frontier in Child Abuse. *Children Today* **4**: 18–21.

Sroufe, L.A. and Ward, M.J. (1980) Seductive Behaviour of Mothers and Toddlers: Occurrence, Correlates and Family Origins. *Child Development* **51**: 1222–229.

Steele, B.F. and Alexander, H. (1981) Long-term Effects of Sexual Abuse in Childhood. In P.B. Mrazek and C.H. Kempe (eds) *Sexually Abused Children and their Families*. Oxford: Pergamon Press.

Summit, R.C. (1983) The Child Sexual Abuse Accommodation Syndrome. *Child Abuse and Neglect* **7**(2): 177–93.

SWSG (1982) Child abuse. SW 4/82 NHS Circular No 1982 (GEN) 18.

Trowell, J. (1983) Emotional Abuse. *Health Visitor* **56**: 252–54.

Tsai, M., Feldman-Summers, S., and Edgar, M. (1979) Childhood Molestation: Variables Related to Differential Impacts on Psychosexual Functioning in Adult Women. *Journal of Abnormal Psychology* **88**: 407–17.

Yates, A. (1982) Children Eroticized by Incest. *American Journal of Psychiatry* **139**(4): 482–85.

Name index

Subject index